Since first appearing in the *Press and Journal* in 1987, the stories of the North-east Scottish village of Stronach have delighted hundreds of thousands of readers every Saturday morning.

In answer to continual requests from fans of Babbie Girn, Erchie Sotter, Kate Barrington-Graham — and the dozens of other characters who call Stronach home — this first anthology collects a dozen of the best stories from the first 100 episodes; adds two full-length stories never before published; a history of the village; gives biographical details of all the principal villagers, and even prints some of their favourite recipes.

Published by **Stronach Media Ltd.**,
Tullynessle, Alford, Aberdeenshire, AB33 8QN

© Norman Harper
ISBN 1 897672 00 4

First edition : October, 1992

DEDICATION

For my big sister

Stronach

Volume One

Stronach Media Ltd.

Contents

Foreword

The cantrips and antics of Babbie Girn, Erchie Sotter, Walter Dreep, Wayne Spurtle and two dozen other residents of Stronach have been regular reading in the Press and Journal for five years now.

Having been brought up in a small North-east village myself, with that peculiar brand of North-east humour, I had been convinced for years that the root material was there for a North-east series of some sort and that the Press and Journal, itself an integral part of North Scottish life, was the ideal vehicle.

But how to marry the two?

It took three days to arrive at the solution. We would report on the daily doings and gossip of a typical North-east village. It took three weeks of wee-sma-oors work (with copious quantities of cocoa and Kit-Kats) to set up the deal and find a suitable correspondent at a suitable location.

Three weeks later, we had gained considerable insight into behind-the-scenes life in various North-east villages (but we promise we won't tell). I was convinced there was mileage in what we were about to do. I presented a proposal to the Editor, who approved it . . . warily, for a newspaper's heritage of 250 years is not to be tampered with lightly.

Episode One of Stronach appeared on August 1, 1987. (It appears later in this book for those of you who are curious).

It seemed reasonably successful, we thought, looking at that first copy of our newly revamped Weekend Journal Saturday section. In newspapers, we often judge success by a lack of complaints. Stronach was successful.

So it ran, week by week, as the principal characters were introduced gradually on our planned basis over the first 24 episodes.

We continued the series over that winter and well into the next summer. We got the occasional approving phone call and a letter now and again inquiring after particular characters, and that was fine.

After Stronach's first birthday, we decided to take stock of Weekend Journal as a whole and, among us, wondered if maybe the Saturday supplement needed a bit more weight and authority. It doesn't do to be too light-hearted and whimsical in a newspaper which has become something of the fabric – a cornerstone – of the area it serves.

We kicked around several ideas and always came back to the perennial problem in newspapers – lack of space. (It's a common fallacy that newspapers are desperate for material to fill their columns. Every issue of the P&J is offered four times as much material as we can use).

In any case, if we were to give Weekend Journal more weight, something had to go. And it had to be something which would cause least upset to our readers.

I suggested Stronach. Yes, me.

It had run for 60 episodes and had served us well, I argued, and the time had come to let Stronach pass away peacefully in her sleep.

In making my recommendation, my principal concern had been that a large part of Weekend Journal was being lost to our many readers in the Highlands and Islands because of the North-east dialect in Stronach.

That fear; our instinct that Weekend Journal needed more weight, and the increasing exhaustion of the clandestine correspondent (for a weekly column quickly becomes a tyrant) made it an easy decision.

An easy decision, but a foolish one.

On reflection, I had misjudged our readership just a thochtie. I had forgotten that we North-easters are slow with our praise until the object of our affections is taken from us.

I'm told the calls started arriving at the Press and Journal switchboard at 8.30 on that first Stronach-less Saturday morning.

The telephonists reported the callers were of varying degrees of courtesy, temper and demeanour, but that the basic, underlying message was always firmly expressed and was always the same:

"Far's Stronach?"

To say I was astonished by the depth of feeling is understatement. Stronach was never meant as anything more than a Saturday-morning amusement to lighten readers' weekends after five days of unmitigated gloom. Yet here were people for whom it had obviously struck a chord.

So, yes, I was astonished, delighted . . . and guilty. I had never murdered before, yet, by my hand, Babbie Girn, Virginia Huffie, Euphemia Pink and all the other Stronachers had been done to death.

When the mailbags were opened throughout the subsequent week, my desk was submerged. Since Press and Journal policy is always to give as many people as possible a forum to express a point of view, even when that view is sometimes directed against us, we printed two.

That simply served to quadruple the number of complaints and, knowing we hadn't a hope of riding it out, the Editor and I convened a hasty meeting to work out a solution.

"Well," he said, "there's only one solution, isn't there?"

Stronach was reinstated, after 13 weeks away, with a Christmas Eve double-length episode in which the village pensioners were celebrating at their Christmas party to the strains of Johnny Fortuno and his Meikle-Wartle Ceilidh Band.

Since then, Stronach has developed beyond all our hopes. Our correspondence is regular and rewarding. Stronach has been used as teaching modules in several North-east secondary schools. It appeared in a course at the Northern College of Education.

Readers have followed the adventures of Stronach's villagers going through teenage romance, engagement, a death, suspected adultery, two births, marriage troubles, unmarried mums, cheeky young children, incompetent outsiders, lusty pensioners, bewildered tourists. . . indeed, everything that goes to make up any North-east village.

And that, we hope, is the root of Stronach's success. Although the stories are simple tales meant just to raise a smile over the Saturday-morning cornflakes, they reflect the foibles and wiles of ordinary North-east folk, albeit with a little embellishment, exaggeration and caricature to point up a few North-east traits and habits.

And that's why, when we are out at functions and someone comes up and starts to speak about the series, we're usually asked something like: "Is Ebenezer Grip the shopkeeper at xxxxxx?" or "Fa's the real Babbie Girn?"

If the characters are that lifelike and real to you, we're flattered and I'm delighted.

The truth is that there isn't a single Ebenezer Grip or a single Babbie Girn. There are hundreds of Ebenezers and thousands of Babbies, Wayne Spurtles, Erchie Sotters and Virginia Huffies living in every North-east corner you care to name. And there's a little of each of them in Ebenezer and Babbie and Geneva.

Even at their most ill-natered, they're the salt of the earth, and none of our hamlets, villages or towns would be the same without them.

So we'll go on charting the lives and times of Stronach and her residents for as long as you would like us to.

Thanks for your enthusiasm and interest. Keep it coming.
And enjoy your book.

NORMAN HARPER
Features Editor,
Press and Journal

October, 1992

Stronach:

the

village

Stronach

An appreciation of a North-east village (1194 – 1992)

By Professor Dr Reginald Knox-Fooshtie
Department of History
University of Old Aberdeen

It is difficult to place Stronach exactly, but studying the Ordnance Survey map shows it to be located approximately 25 miles from Aberdeen, 25 from Peterhead, 25 from Elgin and 25 from Braemar.

It lies at an altitude of 923ft, nestling in a 14sq.m. bowl, surrounded by the Hills of Stronach. There are but two access roads to speak of, both so tortuous they are blocked all too easily in winter. One can be dated back to 1730 when General Ford, an associate of General Wade, took a party of troopers to design and lay a military road through the Howe of Stronach, the better to assist in the control and policing of the warring clans of the area.

It took them more than 14 months to lay five miles of road, not because of the difficult terrain but because, while the soldiers slept, the men, women and children for several miles around would spirit away the best of the stone and dismantle much of that day's road foundations. Those English soldiers were unwitting suppliers of the raw materials for some of the finest croft buildings and cattle-shelters the North-east has ever seen. Indeed, those same buildings and shelters, now having weathered almost three centuries of Stronach winters, can be seen in use in farm closes and at the edges of parks throughout the Howe of Stronach to this day, testament to the quality of craftsmanship and kleptomania which pertained at Stronach more than 250 years ago.

Stronach's history is indeterminate, although it is known to be one of the North-east's oldest settlements, lying at the confluence of the Burn of Stronach and the Water of Bogensharn.

A charter held in the vaults of the Central Library in Aberdeen dates from 1194. It shows that King William I of Scotland, brother of King Malcolm IV, had given "that lands which do lie furth, twixt and foreto Don and Deveron and Dee" to Lord Alexander de Stroinnaigh, Thane of Inverspaver, a nobleman who had assisted in quelling rebellious natives and clans throughout the Laich of Moray, Buchan, Formartine and the Garioch.

As part of the terms of this gift, Lord Alexander was required to establish "a goodlie hamlet, for the care, respite and guid husbandrie of farming fowke such as it please to labour in thae parks and fields". Lord Alexander was true to his word and, save for a difficult time during the stewardship of his great-grandson, Lord William the Black (1222-1274), Stronach has thriven as a prosperous and successful farming community.

It is said that Lord William the Black's reign would have continued for several decades more had it not been for the timely intervention of a fire in a henhouse in which he happened to have been enticed, abandoned in a state of undress, then secured by one of his subjects, a seamstress by the name of Margaret Huffaidh.

Undoubtedly, Stronach's most prosperous times were in the late 18th and early 19th centuries, when the Barons of Stronach built three magnificent mansion houses in the Howe, each occupied in rotation for four months of the year. Their construction, from the granite of two nearby quarries, brought untold wealth and craftsmanship to the village and its surrounds. The lords, ladies and noblemen of Edinburgh and London society were oft to be seen strolling through the leafy lanes and by the babbling burns of Stronach while spending time as guests of the barons and their families.

Mid-Victorian society was scandalised when the wife and daughter of a London nobleman, a guest of the 22nd Baron Stronach, were seduced simultaneously by a gardener at the Manor of Stronach, one Albert Stott Sotter, and were spirited away to "recuperation" in one of the noble houses of England for nine months. It is popularly held that, such was the beauty of Stronach, both women pined for years after for the leafy glades of the howe and soft grasses and warm breezes down by the Burn of Stronach.

To this day, Stronach residents watch avidly all television transmissions from the House of Lords where, they maintain, at least 14 peers bear a striking resemblance to Albert's grandson, Erchie Sotter, former Gordon Highlander, railway shunter and currently a noted authority on the malts of Speyside. Several approaches and requests by Mr Sotter to be permitted to sample and share in his more-elevated relatives' wealth and affluence have so far met with limited success and, at the last count, six solicitors' letters of increasingly stern tone and demeanour.

By the end of Victoria's reign, two of the three houses had been demolished and only the magnificent gothic-baronial House of Stronach, dating from 1843, was left standing. In its 102 oak-panelled rooms had unfolded a panoply of modern North-east history.

However, it survived barely more than 100 years, for when the 25th baron, Sir Jolyon Fortescue-Stronach, found post-war taxes and death duties too onerous, a mysterious fire consumed the house one night in 1951. It has lain a silent ruin for the last 42 years.

Stronach's railway line was ripped up as part of the Beeching cuts in 1965. The passenger service had closed in 1957 and the line was kept open by the freight of agricultural supplies. Slowly, those supplies were switched to cheaper and more-flexible road freight, and the line was declared an inveterate loss-maker. Its fate was sealed. The trackbed can still be followed in parts, although it is now substantially overgrown, and many embankments have been levelled and cuttings filled in to create new farmlands.

Today, as in much of the North-east, farming is still Stronach's main industry, although it is not so labour-intensive as it was. Mechanisation has reduced one-time legions of horsemen, cattlemen, labourers and grieves to just a few dozen farmers and farmhands assisted by ranks of combines and high-tech machinery.

This slow depopulation at the hands of advancing technology has posed Stronach the same dilemma which has faced much of the North-east: dwindling support for the very fabric and infrastructure of rural life. Many of the small country shops around the edges of the Howe have closed as the advance of supermarkets and hypermarkets in Aberdeen has continued relentlessly, and the increasing mobility and ease of car-ownership has made it easier for village families to avail themselves of cheaper prices and greater variety farther afield.

From a peak population of 1,124 in 1901, Stronach is now home to 523 souls, according to 1991 census returns. Demographics show the average age to be 51, which statisticians hold to be quite high. This is attributed to the fact that so many pensioners live in the vale and because so many of Stronach's young people must leave the vale to find work.

Stronach is trying to establish itself as a tourist destination, yet the facilities are few. Two shops, a post office, a paper shop and a primary school do not, as yet, prove much of a crowd-puller, although there is lively business at the Stronach Arms, a small but comfortable hotel with homely food and lively lounge and public bars, where North-east life can be sampled at its most honest. Only the building of a small swimming-pool and the establishment of a caravan site in the mid-1980s are concessions to tourists' needs. As yet, they have not proven themselves convincingly successful, although the villagers declare themselves delighted by the pool. Other villages have cast envious eyes.

There is a lively village social life, however. District-council figures show the Stronach Village Hall (1901) to be the best-used in North-east Scotland. This has given added impetus to the district council's intention to replace the hall's curtains (1947) and lino (1952) as soon as finances become available.

Meanwhile, the WRI, mother and toddlers association, youth club, pensioners' lunch club, country-dance society and bingo club occupy the hall six evenings a week. During school time, it is often used as an overspill classroom for the primary school. Most Saturdays see the hall occupied with a fundraising activity of one sort or another. There are sales of work, daffodil teas, fetes, jumble sales, bring and buys and sundry other communal North-east favourites, all of which attract attention and activity from well beyond the confines of the Howe.

For the moment, Stronach remains a sleepy, quiet, seemingly indifferent community, happy to be bypassed by the general melee and hubbub of contemporary living. To visit Stronach, says the tourist-board leaflet available (free) at the tourist office in Aberdeen, "is to enjoy life as it used to be lived and as it should be lived. A place where everyone knows everyone else, and takes a kindly interest in their welfare and business. A place where, within minutes of arriving, you'll feel your modern-day burdens slipping from your shoulders and you'll feel lighter of step and cheerier of spirit".

This is proven every Saturday morning, when one of Britain's leading regional daily newspapers, the *Press and Journal*, allows outsiders the chance to peer voyeuristically at the daily doings of the people of Stronach thanks to covert dispatches from the very heart of the village. As yet, the villagers are unaware of who is the newspaper's clandestine correspondent.

But when they find out . . .

Stronach:
the
people

BABBIE GIRN

Full name:	Barbara Florentyna McTavish Girn
Maiden Name:	Spyocher
Age:	68
House:	Middle of a terrace of three in Main Street
Marital status:	Widowed in 1979. Husband named Bert, a retired grieve. Babbie now an enthusiastic worker on behalf of the Retired Grieve's Benevolent Fund (Stronach chapter).
Jobs:	Housewife and cantankerous besom
Clubs, Societies:	Stronach Pensioners. Bingo. WRI
Friends:	Virginia Huffie, although "there's whiles she fairly gets on yer wick"
Hobbies:	Cookery. Gardening. Catty comments
Medical History	Substantially overweight, although trying to reduce from a Size 18 to at least a 14. Suspected kidney trouble in 1988, although it turned out to be a bad bout of wind. Tonsils and a wisdom tooth removed in 1988 in a job lot.
Likes:	Take the High Road. Good manners. A richt good news. Jimmy Spankie. June Imray. The Press and Journal (although it's nae the same since they shifted the Deaths aff Page Two. Ye kent far ye were wi the Deaths on Page Two.)
Dislikes:	Bad manners. Kids. Bunions.
Favourite Colours:	Purple and orange, "like in my back bedroom"
Favourite Music:	Johnny Fortuno and his Meikle Wartle Ceilidh Band. Jim Reeves. Perry Como
Relatives:	A niece at Oldmeldrum. A niece, Ambrosia, in council flats at Fraserburgh. A nephew at Tarland who works for British Telecom and does garden homers on the side. Another nephew, Bert, and his wife, Pansy, emigrated from Lonmay to Texas in 1964, and they visited for the first time (minus their triplets) in 1989. Cousin Bertie lives in New Zealand and hasn't been home since he emigrated just after the last war.

Ideal holiday destination:	A caravan at Stonehaven for a week. (Affa fine folk at Stonehaven, especially that nice wifie in the paper shop).
My hero:	Faivver inventit spray-on furniture polish. Tinnies o' beeswax fairly took the good o' yer elbows.
Philosophy on Life:	If ye ask me, I blame the parents. Aye oot at the bingo or the pub. Nivver at hame. Geets roamin the streets packin their faces wi crisps and ice-cream and ither gulshich. It's nae surprise there's vandals. If they peyed mair attention til their bairns and less attention til their throats and their holidays in Spain, I widna hae sweetie papers and fag packets a' ower my bonnie gairden, and we widna hae chikky loons deliverin wir papers in the mornin. Apart fae that, I'm a'richt in masel.
If I were Prime Minister for a Day:	I'd send that dampt white settlers back far they come fae. Comin in here bumpin their gums aboot this, that and the ither. Moanin and whinin aboot facilities for this and standards o' that. Lord, they kent fit like we were afore they came. If they dinna like it, they should keep their faces shut or pack their cases and clear oot. We'd be fine pleased ti see the back o' them, especially them that's aye yatterin aboot things they ken damn aal aboot
Motto:	Keep cheery.

VIRGINIA HUFFIE

Full name: Virginia Margaret Mary Huffie

Maiden Name: Still a maiden, although aye lookin

Age: 67

House: End of a terrace of three in Main Street. Babbie Girn is her next-door neighbour, which has its advantages and disadvantages. Babbie can burst in at the most inopportune times, and she never knocks.

Marital status: Single

Jobs: Housewife and catlover. Spent her youth as a kitchie-deem at Wester Boggiedubs

Clubs, Societies: Stronach Pensioners. WRI.

Friends: Babbie Girn

Hobbies: Cookery. Gardening. Being a doormat.

Romantic history: Not a great fan of men, for "they've got sic affa fool habits", but was once sufficiently charmed by a scrap-metal merchant from Aberdeen to allow him to chaperon her to a stovie dance at Auchterless. Babbie, fearing that her place in Virginia's affections was about to be lost, managed to put the skids on the relationship.

Likes: Take the High Road. A clean hoose. Cullen skink. My cats (Piercy and Big Black Sambo, although it came as a bit of a stammygaster to find that Piercy and Big Black Sambo were brother and sister, but had been playing mummies and daddies, as well. Managed to find a home for all the kittlins, though.

Dislikes: Cat-haters. Dubs on a newly hoovered carpet

Favourite Colours: Pastel pink and powder blue

Favourite Music: Johnny Fortuno and his Meikle Wartle Ceilidh Band. Doris Day. Lena Martell. Will Starr.

Relatives: Doesn't really have any relatives to speak of, although she thinks her deceased brother, Victor, had a waster of a son who is now an insurance agent somewhere in England. Has always had a feeling that she has blue blood in her somewhere, although Babbie just laughs at the very suggestion.

Ideal holiday destination:

Nivver really socht a holiday. Canna leave ma cats, ye see, though I believe there's a guest-hoose at Crieff taks cats, so I'll maybe get roon til't some day.

My hero:

Inverdarroch in Take the High Road, although they're nae ca'in him Inverdarroch noo. Hiv ye noticed?

Philosophy on Life:

Easy come. easy go. I've nivver really hid muckle, so I've nithing muckle til loase. If folk spent less time chasin money and mair time appreciatin fit they've already got, the warld wid be a far happier place, div ye nae think? Mind you, I'm aye hopin for a winnie on the Premium Bonds. A twa-three hunder wid come in richt handy for a rainy day. And there's plenty rainy days at Stronach, as weel ye ken. What an affa day o' rain yestreen, for instance.

If I were Prime Minister for a Day:

I'd ban Austrian blinds for a start. Affa lookin things. Jist stew-collectors. If folk kent how stupid their hooses looked, they widna dream o' pittin them up. And I'd ban shop-bocht jam. There's nithing like a hame-made pot o' rhubarb and ginger, and makkin it's nae that difficult. I dinna ken how folk can pit that Hartley's stuff ower their throats. Ye're nivver sure fit's in it. I ken someb'dy that was a picker on a rasp fairm ae year. He said they did some affa things amon the berries.

Motto:

There's gweed in a'b'dy if ye look hard aneuch

GENEVA BROSE

Full name: Geneva Floretta Vienna Brose

Maiden Name: Soorock

Age: 53

House: Old farmhouse now in the middle of the village

Marital status: Married to Sandy. Two children: Jocky, a pot-scrubber and door-to-door toothbrush salesman in Manchester; Floretta, a graduate of Aberdeen University and fiancee of Sammy Dreep.

Jobs: Housewife and cantankerous besom

Clubs, Societies: Bingo. WRI.

Friends: Nae naeb'dy, really. I likes keepin masel til masel. Ye meet a better class o' person that wye, I aye think

Hobbies: Cookery. Baking. Cuisine. Mair cookery.

Employment History: Was a clippie on the Alexander's bus from Aberdeen to Stronach, but had to take early retirement when her bunions flared up and passengers began complaining about the smell. Met Sandy, who was the bus driver at the time. Sandy has no sense of smell. A perfect couple

Likes: Hiv I said cookery? I like a good cookery programme on the TV, although it really annoys me if they dinna clean oot the bowl. They'll be standing there yatterin til the camera and they hinna half that mixture scrapit oot. There's starvin bairnies in Africa.

Dislikes: The wifie Dreep. I hiv plans for her, though.

Favourite Colours: A deep, rich gold. Jist like in ma Victoria Sponge

Favourite Music: Wagner. I pit on a cassette and I mix up ma choux pastry til Ride o' the Valkyries. What a rare shine ye get on the dough.

Relatives: An only child, although has learned to thole Sandy's brothers and sisters when they pay a visit. Not enamoured of the prospect of becoming a relation to the Dreep clan once Sammy Dreep and Floretta are married. Has tried several times to talk her daughter out of it, but this has only stiffened Floretta's resolve. Now resigned to having "another gawpit clort in the femly"

Ideal holiday destination:	I fancy a romantic springtime in Paris, wi champagne breakfasts and moonlight suppers doon aside the river. Sandy says ye dinna need Paris. Ye get that at Kemnay.
My hero:	Johnny Craddock, the boy wi the monocle that did the cookery programmes on the TV wi Fanny. Now *there* wis a man that aye lookit richt weel-dressed, even fan he wis clartit in batter. And he aye did the washin-up. Did ye notice that? Ilky time, up til his elbows in Sqezy and Fanny drippin wi jools. That's aye appealed til me.
Philosophy on Life:	Ye'll nivver understand a man. Treat them a' lik little laddies in lang troosers and ye're nae far wrang. For instance, I've never understood fit wye men are aye awa at the pub as seen's yer back's turned. They've barely finished washin and dryin the dishes, layin the table for the morn's breakfast and catchin up on the ironin and the darnin – whoosh – ye canna see them for stew and sma steens.
If I were Prime Minister for a Day:	I'd bring in a law that wid ban shell suits. Aren't they affa? They're nae bad if ye're young and sporty and if ye've the figure for them, bit, Lord, ye see some affa targets in Union Street. Aul wifies wi dowps lik twa cushions. Aye, *big* cushions. For a settee. And great big bellies. And they think they're with-it, that's fit gets me.
Motto:	Fit's for ye, winna ging by ye.

SANDY BROSE

Full name: Alexander Clarence Brose

Nicknames: None that he knows of

Age: 55

House: Old farmhouse now in the middle of the village

Marital status: Married to Geneva. Two children: Jocky, a pot-scrubber and door-to-door toothbrush salesman in Manchester; Floretta, a graduate of Aberdeen University and fiancee of Sammy Dreep.

Jobs: Took early retirement from Alexander's buses after a towtruck ran over his accelerator foot.

Clubs, Societies: Bingo. Helper at Stronach Pensioners' Club.

Friends: Walter Dreep. Salt o' the earth. A richt fine chiel. Wid help onybody oot o' a ticht spot. Fit's his is yours. As lang as that disna apply til his wife, that's fine wi me. I've enough on ma plate wi Geneva.

Hobbies: Gardening. Betting. Eating. Sleeping.

Employment History: After National Service, worked as a trainee butcher, but was allergic to blood. Wanted a similar line of work so took a job as a lorry mechanic. Moved to become the mechanic at the Stronach bus garage then graduated to become one of the two village bus-drivers. Found one-man operation difficult because he was never good with money. Still unhappy about decimalisation.

Likes: A half of Guinness every Thursday night. A snooze with the Sunday papers. Horse-racing on Channel 4 every afternoon.

Ambition: To meet Neil Kinnock and tell him what a waste o' space he was. As for that Robin Cook – he's nae a bonnie loonie, is he? He should click up wi that Margaret Beckett, the Labour No.2. It wid save spilin anither couple.

Favourite Music: Tina Turner. Ye widna think she wis 67, wid ye? Efter a performance they tak her hame in a wheelchair, pit her wig in a box, her eyelashes in a drawer, her jewels in a safe, her sheen in a press, her breists in a juggie o' warm watter, then they hing the rest o' her up in a wardrobe.

Ideal holiday destination:

A bittie culture. I wid like to admire the vanishing culture of the American Indians. Ye see that best in the Western deserts, I believe. Nevada, especially. I believe roon aboot Las Vegas is real interestin. Then Europe's vanishing monarchies his aye intrigued me. A puckle days in Monte Carlo wid cover that. And, of course, the social aspects of the British working man at play. A puckle days at Kempton Park or Sandown wid fill me in on that score. Then I dinna think ye should neglect yer ain heritage. For instance, the North-east o' Scotland has really made its mark on the world. I'd hae ti bone up on that, jist for ma ain peace of mind. Well, ye feel richt ignorant, really; nae kennin yer ain back yard. Am I richt? I think I wid start wi bonin up at Dufftown, then I'd maybe tak a tekkie in past Craigellachie, Rothes, Glenlivet, Cardhu, Tamdhu. Placies like that, ye ken. Keep yersel weel-educatit. I've aye believed that.

My hero:

Georgie Best. *There* wis a man that had the lot. Jet-set lifestyle. Sportin ability. Fame. Top hotels. Beautiful women on baith airms ilky nicht. Faist cars. Bricht lichts. Threw the hale jing-bang awa, like, bit it must hiv been great while it laistit.

Philosophy on Life

Dinna let life's little setbacks grind ye doon. Setbacks like wives, kids, femly . . .

Motto:

There's aye a something

AGGIE DREEP

Full name:	Agnes Catherine Susan Dreep
Maiden Name:	Toast
Age:	53
House:	Old cottage in the middle of the village
Marital status:	Married to Walter. One son: Sammy, a graduate of the University of Aberdeen in criminal psychology and industrial pyrotechnology (fibs and squibs). Now a subterranean hygiene operative with Grampian Regional Council (sewerman), but only until he finds something more befitting his talents. Soon to be wed to Floretta Brose. Other son, Danny.
Jobs:	Housewife and cantankerous besom
Clubs, Societies:	Bingo. WRI. Pensioners' club helper
Friends:	Well, of coorse, I'm adored by a' the pensioners at the club. They often say if there wis a prize for helpin pensioners, they'd hope it was a lang holiday. Far awa.
Hobbies:	Cookery. Buying clothes. Slimming clubs
Employment History:	Worked at the school meals, but had to give up when her co-workers complained she was too slow and perfectionist. Primary schoolchildren don't appreciate butter sculptures, they insisted, and the philistines at the education department sided with them. Can you believe it? "I'm nae carin', onywye."
Likes:	Ma cats. Mr Tiddles is jist a treasure. Sits and purrs on yer lap lik a motorboat. And we got a new cattie a while syne. Ca'd it Huggis. Nae because it's little and roon and fat. Because it's nearly bald and it maks an affa smell. Still, ma catties fairly keep doon the mice. And they sharpen their clooks on ma mither-in-law, which she's nae affa happy aboot. Still, she's bedridden so there's nae muckle she can dee aboot it, is there?
Dislikes:	The wifie Brose. I hiv plans for her, though.
Relatives:	Ma mither-in-law, Aul Beldie (Mother Dreep), turned affa nae weel after her man deed, so she bides in wir front bedroom noo. She's bedridden, bit we let her up noo and again if we feel like it and if we've time.

Ideal holiday destination:	A fortnicht in Madeira. I've aye funcied Madeira. I dinna ken fit wye, for I canna spik Madeiran and I've nae relations there. I like their cakes, though.
My hero:	The boy Kenwood. Him that inventit food-mixers. What a blessin that man wis. Afore that, we'd jist widden speens and spurtles. Efter a mornin's bakin, yer elbows went up lik fitbas.
Philosophy on Life:	If ye canna dee someb'dy a good turn, dinna dee nithing. I've lived my hale life that wye. Nae deein nithing for naeb'dy. Believe me, it's the safest wye. Ye dinna get inveigled in ither folk's nonsense. Ye dee someb'dy a good turn and they nivver appreciate it. The few times I've lent a helpin hand, folk look at ye like hens layin razors.
If I were Prime Minister for a Day:	I'd increase the pensioners' Christmas Bonus. It's been £10 since it startit. Fit dis £10 buy nooadays? Nithing. It's an insult mair than onything. It hardly buys a few baggies o' sugar and a tinnie or twa o' syrup. Whoop-de-doo. That nice Mr Major, he'll maybe think twice this year. He's got a kind face, I think. Ye canna see muckle o't ahen that jam-jar spectacles, like, bit his wife's affa nice. Aye smilin. Aye cheery. She'll hae a word in his lugs, I'm sure. Big lugs, aren't they?
Motto:	Dinna flee wi the craws and ye winna get shot

23

MOTHER DREEP

Full name:	Isabella (Beldie) Scatterty Dreep
Maiden Name:	Panjandrum
Age:	92
House:	Front room at the home of her son, Walter
Marital status:	Widow. Husband, Doddie, pre-deceased her in July, 1989. Since then, has moved into the village at her son's insistence. Daughter-in-law is considerably less enamoured of her presence.
Jobs:	Invalid and cantankerous besom
Clubs, Societies:	None
Friends:	All dead and buried. "And they're nae miss." Determined to get telegram from Queen in year 2000.
Hobbies:	Thumping walking stick on floor beside bed. Cultivating an air of ill-naturedness. Being disagreeable with her daughter-in-law (Aggie). Consuming cups of tea. Calling for po.
Employment History:	Kitchie-deem at her parents' farm at Memsie, near Fraserburgh, during and after World War I. Met and fell in love with the second horseman, Doddie Dreep, when he enchanted her with talk of his huge Clydesdale. Married in 1929 after he was promised a term as grieve at Wester Boggiedubs, Stronach.
Likes:	A good argy-bargy. Keeps ye young. Keeps ye active. Keeps ither folk in their place.
Dislikes:	Ma dother-in-law. How Walter got in tow wi a besom like that, I dinna ken. He's nae his mither's loon, that's for sure.
Favourite Colours:	Grey. Black. Navy blue. Dark brown. Onything cheery.
Favourite Music:	Rudy Vallee. Nelson Eddy. Jack Buchanan. Ye dinna hear a lot o' them noo.
Relatives:	Son, Walter. Daughter-in-law, Aggie. Grandsons Sammy and Danny. Disappointed that Walter never amounted to much. Has high hopes of Sammy, if he can get a job that suits his degree in "fibs and squibs".

Ideal holiday destination:	A Sunday on the beach at the Broch, wi a slider, a deckchair, the Picture Post and some Motoring chocolate.
My hero:	Harry Gordon. Now, *there* wis an entertainer. He could mak ye lach. He could mak ye greet. A real comedian. Couldna sing a note, bit ye aye admired him for tryin. Ye dinna get entertainers like Harry noo. If they're nae tellin fool, ory stories, they're actin the goat. If it wisna for Take the High Road, I widna bother wi a TV.
Philosophy on Life:	Behind every man, there's an exhaustit woman. Look at my Doddie. Fan the bottom fell oot o' fairmin in the 1930s and he couldna get a term onywye, I wis there. We startit a little business efter the war and fan that collapsed, I wis there. Fan he crashed his car in 1962 and endit up in the hospital, I wis there. Fan he hid that stroke at the candy-floss stall at the Turriff Show in 1978, I wis there. Fan the ambulance crashed on the road til the hospital, I wis there. Atween you and me, Doddie thocht I wis a jinx.
If I were Prime Minister for a Day	I'd timmer up thon MPs. What targets. Thon's a disgrace. Tie-knots like sparras' legs. Half their supper doon their jaickets. Hair like cats' sookins. And what a dampt racket. A puckle heated backsides nott thonder.
Motto:	Fan ye're fair ferfochen, find yer fooshion.

WALTER DREEP

Full name:	Walter Aloysius Arthur Dreep
Nickname:	Wattie
Age:	64
House:	Old cottage in the middle of the village
Marital status:	Married to Aggie. Two sons: Sammy, a graduate of the University of Aberdeen in criminal psychology and industrial pyrotechnology (fibs and squibs). Now a subterranean hygiene operative with Grampian Regional Council (sewerman), but only until he finds something more befitting his talents. Soon to be wed to Floretta Brose. Older son, Danny.
Jobs:	Underdog and retired postie.
Clubs, Societies:	Bingo.
Friends:	Sandy Brose. My best pal fae schooldays. We grew up thegither. We played thegither. We went coortin thegither. He's been wi me through thick and thin. We fell oot only the once – fan he tried to persuade me against mairryin Aggie. I stuck by her, though. I wisna haein her name sullied by the likes o' Sandy Brose. Na. Lord, if I'd listened til Sandy, I widna be far I am ivnoo. I wish to God I'd listened til him.
Hobbies:	Gardening. Washing dishes. My pipe.
Employment History:	After being a bandsman in the RAF during the latter days of the war, Walter thought he should put his musical talents to good use in Civvy Street. He became a postie.
Likes:	A quiet nicht in, wi ma ironin, ma darnin and ma knittin.
Dislikes:	That new Ariel Liquid.
Favourite Music:	Connie Francis. Doris Day. Kenneth McKellar. Peter Morrison. Your Hundred Best Tunes. James Last. Mantovani. Johnny Fortuno and his Meikle Wartle Ceilidh Band.
Ambition:	To give Aggie a piece of his mind just once. Came close when she forgot to buy his favourite brand of starch.

Ideal holiday destination:

Somewye that offers peace and quaet far awa fae Aggie. I'm nae askin for muckle. I'd jist like jist a twa-three days til masel in a place far life wid be slow and quaet and peaceful and easy compared til bidin in the same hoose as Aggie. The RAF bombin range at Tain wid dee fine

My hero:

My mither. What a marvellous woman she is. She'd a hard life. It's couldna hiv been easy makkin ends meet on a horseman's money. She managed, though. She wis tough. She hid ti be. I admire that. I admire a woman that can be up at 4.30 ilky mornin gettin her man up for his wark, then labours a' through the day – aye, often oot in the parks aside the men – then keepin a hoose and keepin a fairm and keepin a' the kids in maet and claes. And she wis aye last til her bed at nicht. It taks a special woman ti manage a life lik that, and ye winna find onyb'dy nooadays wi the smeddum for it. Ye ken this, my mither nivver knew the meanin o' rest. She wis aye wi her shooder til the grindstone and her nose tee til something else. She hid nivver a minute's peace til hersel. Aye on the go. And she nivver complained. Holidays? She nivver kent the meanin o' the word. She thrived on work and plenty o't. And she did that for forty year that I ken o'. Day in, day oot. Isn't that marvellous? And look at her noo. Bedridden, nae teeth, ill-natered, half-blin and deif. She's marvellous, really.

FLO SPURTLE

Full name: Florence Spurtle

Maiden Name: Orts

Age: 32

House: Semi-detached council house in Main Street

Marital status: Married to Gibby. One son: Wayne. One daughter: Cassandra. Thoroughly exhausted with all three of them.

Jobs: You name it, she does it. Home help, shop assistant, cleaner, barmaid, lollipop lady, wife, mother, housekeeper, laundrywoman, chief cook and bottlewasher. Anything that will bring in an honest pound or two.

Clubs, Societies: Bingo. Mother and Toddlers.

Friends: Ower busy for socialisin.

Hobbies: Making ends meet. Gibby. Cooking sausages.

Employment History: Never really had a chance at a career, as such. Was a bright pupil at Stronach Primary, but fell for Gibby's manly charms despite her better judgment. Has since had to endure chronic cash shortages due to Gibby's perpetual unemployment. Harbours an ambition for further education and aspires one day to run her own business.

Likes: Five minutes' peace and quiet. An evening in front of the TV, with the kids in their beds and Gibby out at the pub. A visit from her sister at Cornhill, when she gets a chance to unburden herself and chat about her woes and worries.

Dislikes: Anyone who makes fun of Gibby.

Favourite Colours: Peaceful pink. Tranquil turquoise.

Favourite Music: Bay City Rollers (still has tartan half-mast trousers and platform shoes). Can Shang-a-lang with the best of them.

Relatives: Sister at Cornhill, who is on call at short notice to sort out marital problems. Sister takes a dim view of Gibby's drinking and lack of employment.

Ideal holiday destination:	Bali for a month. A week in Hawaii. A weekend in the executive suite at Claridge's in London. Two weeks in the Seychelles. A week on the Orient Express. A round-the-world cruise on the QE2. In fact, anything where she can be surrounded by rich people and fancy cars. Gibby understands and has suggested a Sunday trip to Crathie to watch the Queen.
My hero:	Arnold Schwarzenegger. He startit wi nithing and look at him noo. He's got the lot. Money, fame, a career, glamour, stardom – and big muscles. Fit mair could ye need in a man? A' that Gibby's got is the muscles. And they're a' in his heid.
Philosophy on Life:	Life? Fit life? I hinna got a life. I clean, I cook, I scrape and save. Fit life's that? Certainly nae bowl o' cherries. Mair a bowl o' tatties. If Gibby's nae sleepin, he's in his gairden. If he's nae in his gairden, he's at the pub. It gets affa depressin whiles. Affa depressin. A man and twa kids aneth yer feet. Greetin. Wintin fed. Wintin oot ti play. Winna eat veggies. Makkin a mess o' the bathroom. And the kids are jist as bad.
If I were Prime Minister for a Day	I'd mak unemployment illegal. I'd gie a' that Government a taste o' the dole and see foo they like it.
Motto:	Fan ye think ye're at rock bottom, and the only road is Up, it's a sure sign anither tragedy's jist roon the corner.

GIBBY SPURTLE

Full name: Gilbert Albert Spurtle

Place of birth: Floor of lounge bar, Stronach Arms. Father unknown. Stronach Pipe Band a possibility.

Age: 34

House: Semi-detached council house in Main Street

Marital status: Married to Florence (Flo). One son: Wayne. One daughter: Cassandra.

Jobs: Chronically unemployed

Clubs, Societies: None to speak of. Would like to start a club for chronically unemployed, but can't summon the energy to participate.

Friends: Few friends. Most others of similar vintage left the howe long ago to find gainful employment and to capitalise on the quality of education they had at the village school. Often seen drinking with Erchie Sotter and helping Erchie in his garden. Quite chummy with Bopsy-Wopsy, the village's communal mongrel, although doesn't want to encourage this as he feels Bopsy is taking advantage of his better nature

Hobbies: Gardening. Drinking at Stronach Arms. Writing application letters.

Employment History: A somewhat chequered record. Attempt at being an apprentice farmhand ended in disaster when a pig knocked him off a ladder and he landed in hospital. Story made the front page of the Press and Journal. Has applied to become part-time fireman, insurance salesman, double-glazing salesman, door-to-door brush salesman, attendant at a bradie stall and Jehovah's Witness. All rejected as "not quite what we're looking for at this time".

Likes: Ma gairden.

Dislikes: Ma gairden on a fool day.

Relatives: Mother stays in Lancashire, although she visits every four or five years just to keep an eye on Gilbert and the grandchildren. Doesn't particularly care for Flo, which is fine, because Flo doesn't particularly care for her.

Ideal holiday destination:	A weekend at the Chelsea Garden Show. Tatties like boulders and peas like steens. And that's jist how Flo cooks them. Boulders and steens.
My hero:	I hinna really got a hero. I admired the boy that gave me ma first job. Folk telt him he shouldna. Folk said I wis mair trouble nor I wis worth bit, na, he wis his ain man. He made up his mind and he stuck til't. He could see a good employee fan he came across een. So I got the job. Within weeks, I could see him gazin at me wi a proud look on his face. I think it wis proud. Luckily, he wisna kept in Cornhill for lang. He wis oot at the Glen O' Dee in the hinder end. The last I heard, he wis lookin efter sheep near Forsinard.
Philosophy on Life:	A dram, a lach and a good graip and hyow. Ye're a' the wye.
If I were Prime Minister for a Day:	I wid hae a hale TV channel for gairdenin programmes. Ye learn tips aff gairdenin programmes. Beechgrove's nae the same athoot Jim and George, though, is it? I likit Jim and George. Ye got the impression they didna ken nithing ata, bit their tatties aye came up bonnie and the heids on their chrysanths wis like fitbas. They say ither folk did a' the work. I weel believe it. I nivver saw fool hauns on ony o' the twa o' them.
Motto:	Mony a mickle maks a lot o' mickles

WAYNE SPURTLE

Full name:	Wayne Jason Dominic Spurtle
Nickname:	Nobody would dare
Age:	9
House:	Semi-detached council house in Main Street
Marital status:	Single, and fully intends to keep it that way for ever and ever, although was infatuated by temporary teacher Miss Rapunzel Bicker for a while. She did not return the favour.
Jobs:	Schoolboy and professional nickum
Clubs, Societies:	Wayne's Gang. Stronach Primary football team.
Friends:	Pretty much a free spirit, but has been known to get up to mischief with his best friend, Puddick.
Hobbies:	Chasing hens. Pinching apples. Collecting tadpoles. Trailing dubby shoes across newly cleaned kitchen floors. Reading comics.
Employment History:	Tried for a Saturday job at the Stronach Emporium and General Stores as a message-loon, but gave up when Ebenezer Grip insisted he supply his own bike and that he would be paid, literally, in sweeties (two tubes of Rolos and a bar of coo candy).
Likes:	Chocolate. Playing with his food. Mashes up his mince and tatties, heaps it into piles then drives his fork round and round the plate making brrmmm brrmmm noises. Instant Whip is his favourite dessert.
Dislikes:	Kisses fae grandma. Playin wi ma sister. Bathtime.
Favourite Colour:	Red (Aberdeen FC).
Examples of Mischief:	Sent home from Stronach Primary in 1989 for holding a strip-poker tournament behind the bike sheds. Has a love-hate relationship with next door's cat (mostly hate). Stretched clingwrap over the public toilets in 1990. Froze tadpole spawn last year and slipped it into the Christmas trifle (father complimented his mother on her blackcurrant jam). Put shaving foam in his mother's slippers. Volunteered to provide the eggs for the school's Easter fun day. He scrambled them first.

Ideal holiday destination: Disneyland. Failing that, any funpark with a roller-coaster that makes you really sick. Not just *feeling* sick. Really spewing.

My hero: My dad. My mither says he's jist a big bairn, really. Bit he's great fun. It wis him that learned me that clingfilm's OK for cookery, bit it's far better for stickin ower the heid o' a lavvie. It wis him that put shavin foam in ma granny's slippers. I got the row, like, bit I didna mind. Ye feel sorry for him, in a wye.

Philosophy on Life: Enjoy yersel. There's ower mony folk wi lang faces and soor mous tellin ye fit ye can and fit ye canna dee. My dad says it disna stop fan ye're aul, eether. Jist ignore them a'. If deein fit ye're telt maks ye look lik them, I'd rether spend a' ma siller and hae a rare time.

If I were King for a Day: I'd gie kids a Christmas bonus — £10 worth o' sweeties. Maybe even £20. Mak that £25. My dad says pensioners get a Christmas bonus. Why nae the kids? Pensioners dinna appreciate their bonus; they jist go aboot wi faces like hens' backsides complainin aboot sna and loud music and fitbas landin in their gairdens. Kids wid really appreciate a Christmas bonus. And we wid a' vote for the Prime Minister, I promise. Cubs' Honour. Honest we wid. Cross ma hert. Honest.

Motto: When all about you are losing the heid, be awkward.

KATE BARRINGTON-GRAHAM

Full name:	Katharine Amanda Victoria Barrington-Graham.
Maiden Name:	Barrington
Age:	49
House:	Bridge House, a distinguished five-bedroom villa in its own three acres, two miles beyond the far side of the village. Paddock for the ponies. Steading converted into a three-car garage for the Volvo Estate, the Mercedes and the Volkswagen Golf.
Marital status:	Married to Godfrey, financial analyst with his own oil-related practice in Aberdeen. Two children: Piers, at Oxford reading political economy, and Octavia, at boarding school in the Lake District.
Jobs:	Housewife, retired debutante and professional snob.
Clubs, Societies:	Friends of the Royal Opera House. Campaign to Protect Rural England. Save the Children (gives big donations and gets a mention in their newsletter at Christmas). Chairperson of Stronach Community Council.
Friends:	No one locally. It doesn't do to get too familiar, except in an organising capacity; the locals seem to have very little inclination to organise anything or anyone on their own account. A decent gymkhana would be quite beyond them. They appreciate being led, however. And they certainly appreciate strong leadership.
Hobbies:	Opera. Tapestry. Being condescending.
Employment History:	Has never really had gainful employment, but used to host society dinners for her father after her mother died. Husband Godfrey earns more money than she can handle. Their wealth seems to be a popular topic of conversation among those quaint village people. All most satisfying.
Likes:	Being envied.
Dislikes:	Living so far from a decent patisserie.
Favourite Colours:	Titian.
Relatives:	No one *you'd* have heard of, dear, but all eminent.

Ideal holiday destination:	A quiet weekend in the Cotswolds, with a trip up to London to shop at Fortnum's, with maybe a night at the opera or the ballet.
My hero:	Oh, that's *so* difficult. There are so many heroes of mine. Johnny Black-Spiffington (Spiffers) is *such* a splendid dancer. His feet are poetry. Bubbles Rothermere holds quite the best parties. In history, I admire Churchill, of course – *such* a great, great man. And Mrs Thatcher. In fifty years, people will look back and see what a *great* woman she really was. Oh, and I have more than a sneaking regard for Edward I and the Duke of Cumberland. Such vision. Such drive.
Philosophy on Life:	Never discuss money with people who have a lot less than you. It will only cause problems. *Hint*, by all means, but never discuss it.
If I were Prime Minister for a Day:	I would abolish that ridiculous inheritance tax. Plays havoc when old Lord so-and-so dies and you simply *know* a simply *lovely* house is going to have to go on the market and will probably be bought by some dreadful Cockney upstart scrap-metal merchant with an O-Level in woodwork and a dreadful little wife with bleached hair and a Ford Escort convertible and a Jacuzzi. Dreadful, dreadful, dreadful.
Family motto:	Nihil illegitimis carborundum

DOROTHY BIRZE

Full name:	Dorothy Mima Birze
Maiden Name:	Clashbags
Age:	62
House:	Pensioner's council house in Inverspaver Court
Marital status:	Widowed. Moved from Methlick to get away from old memories and a large grocery bill.
Personal attributes:	Kind heart and short-sightedness
Clubs, Societies:	Bingo. WRI.
Friends:	Finding it difficult to mix into a new community at her age, although the fact that she can barely see anyone doesn't help. Has been observed to develop an animated conversation with the bus stop, and has occasionally complimented the postbox outside the school on "a bonnie reed frockie ye're weerin the day".
Hobbies:	Cookery. Baking. Standing outside the phone box. Sitting in doctor's waiting-room, conversing with invalids.
Employment History:	Has never really had a job, but used to look after neighbours' cats at Methlick when the neighbours went on holiday. Says she can prove eight out of 10 cats don't prefer Whiskas; they prefer pottit heid.
Likes:	Robbie Shepherd. Coronation Street. My Weekly. Pandrops. Coo candy. Stovies. Skirlie (with the onions burned). Swiss milk toffee.
Dislikes:	Caul kail het.
Favourite Colour:	Sharny green. It hides the dirt.
Favourite Music:	A richt birlin dance band, especially at a waddin. Fairly maks yer chikks rosy, and pits colour in yer face, as weel.
Relatives:	Few relatives to speak of. Has a son who is rumoured to have spent some time in prison, although no one knows for sure. Keeps her husband's ashes in a small urn. "Jist a potta stew on the mantelpiece." Says that, at last, after 40 years of marriage, she knows where the old devil is at nights.

Ideal holiday destination:

A week in a caravan at Lossie, followed by a week at a B&B at Turriff. Unfortunately, can afford neither, so spends her time watching travel programmes on the TV.

My heroes:

The postie; he cuts ma grass in the summer. The milkie; he cleans ma windies. The coalman; he sweeps little pathies through the sna in the winter. I did try sweepin ma ain pathies in the sna, bit I endit up three gairdens doon the road and the wifie there wisna affa chuffed aboot me pittin oot ma washin on her line.

Philosophy on Life:

If ye can keep cheery aboot yer mistakes, ye'll be a' richt. I mak plenty o' mistakes and I dinna mind admittin them. At the cat's feedin time last Tuesday, I opened a tinnie for her. I couldna mak oot the label and, the lucky little pussy that she is, she got a hale tinnie o' best steak mince and peas that I'd been savin for a special occasion. Lucky, lucky pussy. I didna find oot until twa days later. My tea wis a softie and syrup and a plate o' Whiskas wi rabbit chunks. It's tastier than ye think, that Whiskas. Nae dry ata. And fine big chunks. I tak mine wi a bit beetroot and a tomata. Jist smashin.

If I were Prime Minister for a Day:

I'd be able til afford a new pair o' glesses. What a difference it wid mak. I've only ma pension, ye see, and a pension disna pit ye far in the road.

Motto:

Better days roon the corner.

EBENEZER GRIP

Full name:	Ebenezer Jacob Scrooge Grip
Maiden Name:	Dinna be funny
Age:	93
House:	Flat above Stronach Emporium and General Stores
Marital status:	Widower. Loved his wife deeply. Once, when they were in their late 70s, they were involved in a road accident at Dunecht. She devotedly kicked out two of his teeth to increase the insurance claim.
Jobs:	Village shopkeeper and professional miser
Clubs, Societies:	Grampian Speechmaking Society. Stronach Small Business Association (chairman, secretary, treasurer, chief executive and sole member).
Friends:	Erchie Sotter. Although Erchie's aye on the mooch, Ebenezer likes the challenge.
Hobbies:	Speechmaking. Hanging on to siller.
Employment History:	Parents owned the village emporium, which he now owns and runs. Was one of the first RFC pilots in World War I and is never slow to remind people he once saved the lives of 231 Gordon Highlanders. (Accidentally landed on the cook).
Likes:	Making money.
Dislikes:	Spending money. Charity collections. Do-gooders.
Favourite Colours:	Blue, deep-beige, purple, pale green and salmon pink. (Coincidentally, the colours of the major Scottish banknotes). Salmon pink is his personal favourite.
Favourite Music:	Doesn't like music. Distracts people from spending money and also costs electricity to run. Prefers whistling or the 'ding' of the cash register. Music to his ears.
Relatives:	Adopted son, Alick, is the Stronach policeman, soon to retire. Other son, Sid, is retired colonial policeman in Kenya, having emigrated there at the time of the Mau-Mau crisis. Grandson, Dod, served with distinction in the Gulf War as a pilot. Great-grand-daughter, Sharon, in Wayne Spurtle's class at Stronach Primary.

Ideal holiday destination:	Ahen the coonter at the emporium, or a Wednesday aifterneen at the cash and carry. Shopkeepers canna tak holidays, ye see. They maun mak their money.
My hero:	Robert Maxwell. He maybe wisna a bonnie loon, bit what a talent that man hid for business. Bunks, pinsion funds, big corporations – they fell ower themsels shovin siller at him, and he jist took it a' wi a "thank-ye kindly". The bunks chase ye for a twa-three poun over-draft. What a chasin they've got on their hands noo, eh?
Philosophy on Life:	Shopkeepers provide a service. Folk depend on ye. Ye're nae jist a shop til them; ye're mair a social necessity, I aye think. Part o' the infrastructure o' the community. Ye're an essential. Folk drap by and ye maun be there for them. They tell ye their troubles and their worries. Ye offer advice. Ye listen. Ye pint them in the richt direction. They look up til ye. They look for yer wisdom and yer opinion. Ye're nae jist a shop. Ye canna jist shut that aff for twa wikks in the summer. Fit wid they dee? Fa wid they turn til? Far wid they go for advice in their time o' need? Fa wid help them oot o' a crisis in their darkest oor? Answer me that, Also, they spend an affa wheen o' money and ye can fleece them richt, left and centre.
Motto:	Keep the Sabbath and a'thing else ye can lay yer hands on.

ERCHIE SOTTER

Full name:	Archibald Stott Sotter
Maiden Name:	Are you wintin a clap in the lugs?
Age:	76
House:	End of a terrace of three. Babbie Girn is his neighbour.
Marital status:	Widowed, although wife, Edna, left him long before the bus ran her over outside Isaac Benzie's in Aberdeen and distributed her liberally across George Street. His forty years of philandering finally persuaded her to move out.
Jobs:	Professional tapper and mooch
Clubs, Societies:	Stronach Domino League. Bingo.
Friends:	Ebenezer Grip mainly, but will gladly befriend anyone with deep pockets and a raging thirst.
Hobbies:	Angling. Telling stories. Pretty women.
Employment History:	Fee'd at Western Boggiedubs between the wars, but signed up when World War II declared and asked to be posted to anywhere with women. Ended up on the Arctic convoys. Manage to wangle a posting to Normandy at the time of the D-Day landings. Substantial numbers of North-west French elderly women now speak with a Doric accent. Post-war career as engine-driver and shunter on the Stronach branch line.
Likes:	The challenge of helping show strangers and tourists the full panoply and majesty of Scotland that is to be found in the nation's distinguished range of single malts. The look of appreciation on their faces as they discover new tastes, flavours and bouquets. The warm glow of profuse thanks and other folk's whisky.
Dislikes:	Closing time.
Favourite Colours:	The deep, rich gold of a full glass of The Macallan
Favourite Music:	Glenn Miller. (Erchie was a demon jitterbugger).
Relatives:	Son, Stanley, and daughter-in-law, Evie, who run a boarding house at Portsoy. Estranged sister-in-law, who lives in Ferryhill, Aberdeen. Cousin Peterie, who is in an eventide home. Two-thirds of Cherbourg.

Ideal holiday destination:	Two weeks at Portsoy, pearl o' the Banffshire coast. Also, it disna cost me nithing because ma loon's got a boardin-hoose there.
My hero:	Captain of the SS Politician. What a richt public-spirited chiel. Put his ship on til the rocks fine and handy for the locals. A hale cargo o' whisky washed up on yer ain doorstep. What a dream. An inspiration til a hale generation, I dinna mind tellin ye. I'm aye hopin the beer larry gets a puncture ootside ma hoose some Thursday mornin and coups the hale lot in ma gairden. I'd easy help oot rescuin the bottles. I'd hae ti be quick afore the bobbies got there. Ye ken fit bobbies are like. They tak a dim view o' folk helpin tidy up fan a larry coups its load. Less for them.
Philosophy on Life:	A' the world's problems could be solved sittin doon in the pub for a news. We manage it a' the time at the Stronach Arms. And it gets easier as the nicht weirs on.
If I were Prime Minister for a Day:	I'd scrap the tax on whisky. The Government nabs near the hale price o' a bottle in tax. What a swick. If they did awa wi that tax, what a happy population they'd hae. In fact, we'd a' be permanently happy. Then we widna notice the backside they're makkin o' rinnin the country.
Motto:	A frien that treats ye is a treat o' a frien.

Stronach:
the
stories

Romeo Erchie Sotter

Episode 1 : August 1, 1987

THE two women standing next to each other on the steps of Stronach Village Hall made an amusing study. To the left stood the large and imposing figure of Mrs Geneva Brose, determined to be among the first into the Stronach Spring Sale of Work.

To the right was slim and attractive Claire Macfarlane, a newlywed who had just moved to the village from her native Aberdeen and was conscious of how out of place a city-dweller was in so tight-knit a community.

The event meant a great deal to both women. To Claire, it was important to dive straight into the social life of her new village. To Mrs Brose, the fact that she was escorting a newcomer to Stronach raised her status in the community by several points.

And as they swam through the crowds flowing into the hall, they soon found themselves standing next to the confectionery stall amply manned by Mrs Dolly Bosie. "Gie's twa bugs o' yer honey lumps, Dolly," commanded Mrs Brose, and the large, beaming Dolly Bosie cheerfully scooped two fat handfuls of her home-made confection into plastic bags and offered them to her customers. Claire smiled at Mrs Bosie and rejoined her guide as they walked down the stalls.

They had almost reached the far end of the hall when Claire noticed a gnarled, bent old man sitting slumped and half-dozing on a wooden settle in the corner.

"He looks as if life has dealt him a rough hand," observed Claire, and Mrs Brose peered through crowds of beefy women to see who her charge meant.

"Fa? Erchie Sotter?" she said. "It's the price o' him. In his day, he wis een o' the biggest womanisers in Stronach — aye, and for miles roon forbye. Nithing in skirts wis safe. The Stronach Pipe Band near went defunct for wint o' men. Naeb'dy wid jine for fear they bumpit intil Erchie Sotter on his wye hame fae the pub and he mistook the kilt for a frock."

Claire popped another honey lump into her mouth. "It's hard to believe that poor, ill-kempt old codger has a reputation as a Casanova," she said.

"Oh, that's nae the half o't," said Mrs Brose. "He wis in Frunce the time o' the D-Day landins. Fan the rest o' the Allies wis near in Germany, Erchie wis still in Normandy romancin a' thon French quines. There's some says there's little Sotters a' ower Frunce thanks til Erchie's war effort."

"Oh, really, Mrs Brose," said Claire. "I can't believe that such a pathetic creature was the cavalier you claim him to be. Look at him, slumped there on his walking-stick, half asleep."

"Romance ivry nicht," whispered Mrs Brose conspiratorially. "It's nae muckle winder he's conniched. Aye, the chuckens his fair come hame ti roost for Erchie Sotter, and nae mistake."

"Well, I'm going to talk to him if no one else will," announced Claire. "I'll offer him one of Dolly Bosie's splendid honey lumps to try to cheer him up."

"Ye're takkin an affa chunce," warned Mrs Brose as her charge walked off through the crowds. "There's a lotta divvlement in Erchie Sotter yet."

Her warnings were lost in the hubbub of the hall, however, for Claire was already pushing through a melee of burly women fighting over old cardigans, cellophaned plates of caramel squares and pots of lemon curd.

Then, all at once, Claire broke through at the far side of the hall and found herself inches from the old man. He raised his bent head and looked at her weakly.

She took a step forward and stretched out a hand of friendship; a hand containing the bag of sweeties. He looked up at her.

"Honey lumps?" she said.

"Aye," said Erchie. "That's me."

Burglar at the Broses

Episode 3 : August 15, 1987

WITH a cheery wave, Sandy Brose waved goodbye to his golfing cronies, promised them a leathering the following Tuesday and started up the garden path.

He thought he heard a mild wailing as he approached the front door, but he assumed his wife, Geneva, was watching a particularly heart-rending episode of Take the High Road.

As his key turned in the front door, however, he noticed the scratch marks around the lock and on the door handle and he realised something serious was afoot.

He rushed into the living-room to be confronted by his wife and village spinster Miss Virginia Huffie sitting on the sofa, sobbing and trying to comfort each other.

A tear-stained Geneva looked up at her husband standing in the doorway. "Jist lik a man," she wailed. "Nivver aboot fan ye need them."

"I'll second that," mewed Miss Huffie, who was known still to be searching for a husband, despite her 62 years.

Sandy Brose surveyed the scene of devastation before him. Pictures were askew on walls; drawers had been pulled out of cabinets and their contents strewn across the floor, and his wife and Miss Huffie were sitting amid it all, sobbing bitterly.

Summoning all his powers of observation, Sandy drew himself up to his full 5ft10in and declared: "Something's happened."

Geneva Brose threw her man a withering look. "Aye, Sherlock," she snapped. "We've been burgled. We've been robbed. We've been taen for a coupla mugs. A' wir earthly goods that you endowed me wi — vanished."

This brought renewed wailing from Miss Huffie. She crossed and uncrossed her legs as if in mortal torture, and only a comforting, beefy arm thrown round her shoulder by Geneva seemed to take away the sting.

Between Virginia's sobs, Geneva revealed that the two of them had caught the burglar red-handed, in broad daylight and, for their pains, had been manhandled roughly along the lobby and thrown into the cupboard under the stairs, where the felon locked them and where they remained while he finished his handiwork.

"Intil a press lik a coupla dusters," raged Geneva, furious at the indignity. "He wis really roch wi's."

Miss Huffie looked up from a teary sob. "Aye," she said, brightening, "he wis quite roch wi's, wisn't he?"

"We wis hostages," barked Geneva, as if to remind her companion of the indignity of their ordeal, and to impress upon Sandy how lacking he had been in husbandly duties through failing to protect the Brose homestead.

Sandy, however, was beginning to grasp the gravity of the situation. He had read about this in the Press and Journal. On TV, he had seen sickening and graphic news stories of assault on innocent women — of any age. He frowned a concerned frown and took a step forward.

"He didna . . ." he stuttered. "Ye ken . . . he didna . . . like . . . touch ye or nithing?"

"Dinna be feel," barked his wife, while Sandy was sure he heard Virginia whisper: "Mair's the peety."

"So fit his he taen?" asked Sandy. Geneva scowled anew. "Fit his he taen?" she snorted. "Fit his he taen? Fit his he nae taen; that's mair til the pint. He's got jist aboot a'thing that's worth onything. We're ruined. On wir uppers. We're cleaned oot.

"Your monogrammed golf ba for best Stronach veteran — that's awa. The crystal Loch Ness Monster that Babbie Girn took back fae Nairn — it's awa. My best-dumplin medal fae the

Stronach Show — awa. It's things lik that ye canna replace."

"It's things lik that ye dinna really wint ti replace," thought Sandy, but he decided discretion was the better part of valour and chose to maintain a diplomatic silence.

Geneva held up a shaky palm and Sandy peered into it to see two solitary strings of pearls and a wedding ring. "This is a' I've got left," she whined. Sandy thought his wife was about to break down again as her shoulders gave a mighty heave and she stammered: "And I've only got them because o' quick thinkin afore the burglar noticed them.

"The only reason we've got my weddin ring and my good pearls fae Untie Belle is because me and Virginia hid them in wir mou's."

Sandy paused. "A peety yer mither wisna here," he muttered. "We could hiv saved the hi-fi, as weel."

Cedric has another

Episode 4 : August 22, 1987

IT WAS a pleasant August Saturday morning and Stronach's reluctant spinster, Miss Virginia Huffie, was out in her front garden tending roses.

Across the fence, Mrs Babbie Girn, commonly perceived as the grumpiest woman in the Vale of Stronach, was howking at dreels of tatties while muttering and cursing under her breath.

Occasionally, she raised her head, adjusted her hairnet and scowled around her before bending down and attacking the potatoes with renewed vigour.

By good fortune — or good timing — Miss Huffie's pauses did not coincide with Babbie Girn's. At least, they did not coincide until shortly before lunchtime, when both women heard footsteps coming up the pavement and looked up to see who was approaching.

It was none other than the village jeweller, Mr Cedric Priss, who had closed his shop for a half-day and was now making his way home to his wife and family.

As he approached the two women, the nattily dressed Mr Priss smoothed down his greying hair, adjusted his tie and nodded in their direction.

"Good morning, ladies," he said. "And isn't it a lovely morning?" Babbie and Miss Huffie laughed politely and Mr Priss walked on down the road.

"Dinna you 'good-mornin' me, ye ory, fool mannie," hissed Babbie while Mr Priss was still barely out of earshot. Miss Huffie, rather taken aback, stared at her neighbour.

"I've aye thocht on Cedric as an attractive sort o' a lad," she confessed, smoothing her greying hair and looking wistfully at the object of her unrequited passions as he strolled off into the distance. "He reminds me on that Tyrone Power . . . in a fermer-chiel kinda wye."

She propped herself up on the shaft of her rake, stared idly and dreamily into the middle distance and fluttered: "Tyrone . . . He wis an affa Tyrone, wisn't he? Looks that wid melt yer hert at fifty paces. Mr Priss is a bittie lik that."

Babbie leaned out over her garden railings to get a full view of the receding figure of Mr Priss. She made a show of considering him for a few moments, then looked back at Miss Huffie. "Canna see't masel," she said.

"Did ye nae ken he's expeckin again? A' he needs is ae mair bairn and he's got a fitba team. Nine ivnoo and anither een come May. Aye, there maun be plenty siller in joollery."

"Mercy be here," gasped Miss Huffie, half in astonishment and half in admiration. "His tenth kiddie? He fairly starts the day on an egg, I'll bet."

"Nivver mind eggs," said Babbie. "That gadgie there's far too frisky for his ain good. High time he put his troosers on back ti front, and that's a fact."

"Nine bairns," mused Miss Huffie. "Well, well, well . . . nine bairns . . ."

"It's his wife I feel sorry for," said Babbie. "She's nae seener draan breath than – BOWF – the hale thing starts again. Peer quine hisna a meenit til hersel."

Babbie and Miss Huffie bent down to restart their horticulture but almost immediately, both stood up again to carry on the conversation.

"He's aye been the same," said Babbie. "Ye could nivver walk the streets for fear Cedric Priss wis on the prowl. My mither aye said that fitivver lassie took on Cedric Priss wid need a gweed, strong back and fine, sturdy hips for plenty bairns. The only compensation wis his uncle haein the biggest fairm in the vale."

Then a thought struck her. "Of coorse, ee were the kitchie-deem at Wester Boggiedubs, weren't ye, Virginia? You were there the same time he wis cattleman. You must ken mair aboot Cedric nor ony o's." And she left an ominous pause, intended to draw out her neighbour.

"He wis a perfect gentleman," snapped Virginia. "A' the time I kent him, he nivver put a fit wrang. He lookit efter that hale byrefae o' nowt day and nicht lik he really cared aboot them aa. They were lik bairnies til him.

"I mind fine the time his uncle wis plannin on sendin the bull til the knackery because it wis past its peak. Cedric sent aff til London for some queer-lik mixture for makkin't – ye ken – frisky again."

She paused for a moment, as if a thought from all those years ago had just struck her.

"Mind you," she said, hesitating, "I aye thocht it wis queer that he took the bottle intil his bedroom ilky nicht instead o' leavin it in the byre."

"That's it," said Babbie. "I telt ye. The bull wisna the only beast gettin a drappie tonic. Cedric wis drinkin that tonic himsel. The fool, ory clort. It's nae surprise he's got kids ower the heid. Fit like a tonic wis it?"

"Well," said Virginia, "I dinna ken exactly.

"Bit I aye thocht it tastit lik liquorice."

A bittie culture

Episode 5 : August 29, 1987

AS IS common in many North-east villages, it is custom at Stronach for housewives to call on each other for an afternoon cuppa and a chat. Copious amounts of tea are drunk and considerable numbers of cakes and biscuits are dispatched while absent friends are taken in hand and their problems and foibles dissected in minute and satisfying detail.

It was at just such an occasion that Geneva Brose found herself playing hostess to the equally formidable Babbie Girn. Both women were observing the etiquette of the occasion, but each knew the other's nature only too well, and each was eager not to be seen to be too submissive.

"Tak anither funcy, Babbie," urged Geneva, pouring herself a heatie-up from the teapot by the fire. "You're een wi nae need for worryin aboot her figure."

Babbie stopped in the middle of a particularly large mouthful of Battenburg, pleasantly amazed by what Geneva had said. She preened herself and reached for two slabs of ginger sponge.

"Aye," said Geneva, looking out poignantly at the street, "ye should hiv startit worryin a lang time afore noo. Ye've left it ower late."

Social niceties would have fallen away rapidly at that point had not a knock come at the door. The bird-like Miss Virginia Huffie let herself in and, with a cheery: "Coo-eee! Only me!", she made her way along the hall.

"Nae this aul craw again," muttered Geneva. "A' we'll hear is men, men, men. She's 62, for ony sake. His she nae got them oot o' her system yet?"

But a glower from Babbie stopped Geneva in midstream. By the time Virginia entered the room bearing her plastic ice-cream box full of double shortbread, Geneva and Babbie were the picture of hospitality and bonhomie.

A few moments later, all three were seated round the fire, each with a cup of tea and Babbie with a fistful of fruit loaf.

"Well, hiv ye been til the art gallery?" asked Geneva. Virginia looked genuinely surprised. "We hinna got an art gall'ry," she said.

"We hiv noo," said Geneva. "A mobile caravan fae the toon. Thon community-council wifie – the dame that's been here twa month – asked the toon gallery for a shottie o't. She thocht Stronach could be deein wi a bittie culture, so they've sent oot a larryload o' picters and statues."

"Hiv you been?" asked Virginia.

"Aye," said Geneva. "Me and Sandy took a tekkie in past this mornin. There's nae much o' nithing, really. Sandy says it's jist copies. He says thon's nae the richt Mona Lisa.

"And he's sure the Lachin Cavalier's in London or Paris or Rome or somewye. He wis intendin askin for his money back till I remindit him he hidna peyed nithing in the first place."

"The Mona Lisa?" said Babbie through a mouthful of tea and currants. "That's the dame wi fit they ca the Enigmatic Smile."

"Wis that her?" gasped Geneva. "Well, Sandy jist said she lookit lik a hen layin razors."

"Fit's that famous statue again?" puzzled Babbie. "The great tall lad in marble." She thought for a few seconds more then she brightened. "Michelangelo's David," she said triumphantly. "That's him. David. A young muscly lad. Nae a stitch on."

Virginia choked loudly and violently on her tea, which drew a hefty slap on the back from Geneva and almost forced her to the floor.

"Aye," said Geneva in mid-chew. "Bare-nakit. Nae a stitch o' nithing on. Nae a happie-up o' nae kind."

THAT evening, after late-night shopping at Stronach Emporium and General Stores, Virginia bumped into Geneva. "Well, Virginia," said Geneva, "did ye nip roon by the art gallery?"

"I did that," said Virginia. "There's some rare things on show."

"And fit did ye think o' thon David lad?"

"A great work o' art," pronounced Virginia. "Affa sensitive sculptit, wi great artistic insight and some rare bits o' chisellin.

"And marble's a lot cauler than I thocht."

51

Geneva's midnight mission

Episode 17 : November 21, 1987

FOR as long as Stronach could remember, Geneva Brose's fruit cake had won the prize at the annual Vale of Stronach baking competition, held every November.

It was moist, light and fruity. "A bit like masel," Geneva quipped every year to whoever happened to be judging. But on the night before the competition, the Brose oven gave up the ghost. It had baked its last buttery; produced its last pavlova, and cooked its last cloutie.

A call to the 24-hour emergency-service number revealed a dire lack of spare parts for a 1952 Creda Zephyr. With a few phrases whose fruitiness matched the would-be cake, Geneva had slammed down the phone on the sleepy engineer.

Now she faced a dilemma. Her reputation was at risk, yet she had no way of cooking this year's award-winning cake. Neither would she affront herself by asking a shottie of someone else's kitchen. Besides, an unfamiliar oven could be the ruin of her. Her old Creda was her lucky charm, her faithful friend.

She lay in her bed that night, tossing and turning, imagining the cruelty of the grins, cackles and laughs of Aggie Dreep and Babbie Girn as the judges announced her withdrawal.

It was barely 4am when Geneva slipped out of bed, still unslept, and rifled the keys for the car from Sandy's pockets. She crept downstairs. She dressed quickly in the living-room and stole out of the back door into the morning blackness. She was heading many miles away, towards Huntly and the finest baker of fruit cakes besides herself.

She bowled up at the bakery shortly before 5.45 and looked furtively about her. Only a milk float buzzed along the street; the potholes in the road rattling the bottles.

She turned up her collar, unsure that even the great distance between Stronach and Huntly, and the earliness of the hour, would prevent her from meeting someone she knew. She rapped on the side door of the bakery and, in just a few moments, a hearty fellow swathed in flour up to his oxters stood there beaming.

"Aye aye, darlin," he boomed. "Fit's yer pleasure? Or should I nae ask?"

"Turn aff the charm ony time ye like," snapped Geneva, pushing past him and into the heavy heat of the bakehouse. A dozen delicious smells of fresh, yeasty breads, rolls and cakes enveloped her.

"I'm needin a fruit slab," announced Geneva. "Ye've got a fair reputation, I'm hearin. A nine-inch square wid dee. And I'd be as weel tak a puckle baps."

The baker looked at his watch. "This must be a fair emergency," he said. "It's nae six o'clock yet. Are ye hungry or can ye nae sleep? Or are ye pregnant?"

"Nivver you mind, ye chikky monkey," said Geneva. "Jist gie's ma fruit slab and ma baps and I winna trouble ye. I can see ye're busy."

Duly reprimanded, the baker collected the items, bagged them and offered them to Geneva. "I dee a rare birthday cake," he said. "Bonny icin and a'thing. Seems an affa waste o' a fine fruit slab, nae pittin some icin on it."

"I said nivver you mind," snapped Geneva, holding out a fiver with one hand and demanding the bags with the others. She was impatient to be home.

The baker scratched his head, but his face broke into a floury grin. "Aweel, lass," he said. "There ye go. Het and steamy. A bit like masel."

Geneva thrust her money at him and was gone. She didn't wait for change. Before the baker had finished wondering at the daftness, Geneva was heading for the Huntly city limits.

LATER that morning, the fruit slab duly jammed, marzipanned and iced, Geneva began preparing for yet another triumphant entrance at the competition.

She was convinced that the bouquet of the flavourings in her marzipan, and the hint of whisky in the apricot jam would mask the difference in taste from her usual cake. As she lay back in her bubble bath, she began planning her acceptance speech.

An hour later, she took the cake from the living-room table, where the gentle heat of the fire had dried out the icing nicely. She gave herself a squirt of the perfume Sandy had given her for their anniversary, Naughty Dreams, and carried the cake out to the car.

AS GENEVA unveiled her cake to the admiring stares of most of the village hall, even Babbie Girn and Aggie Dreep had to stifle their wonderment. This was as close to a work of art as any housewife can get with an icing bag. It was beautiful.

It was hard for Geneva not to puff with pride, for she could almost hear the gnashing of teeth around her. She looked disdainfully at some of her rivals' work.

"Is that fairy cakes?" she asked brightly of Babbie. "There's surely some gey tubby fairies gaun aboot nooadays.

"And is that a Victoria Sponge?" she inquired of Aggie. "Victoria surely widna hiv been affa amused fan she saw that een."

"Wheesht yer yatterin," hissed Babbie. "Here's the judge."

"Fa is't this year?" asked Geneva, smoothing down her dress and hitching up her stays.

"Dampt if I ken," said Aggie. "Some baker fae Huntly."

53

An inspector calls

Episode 26 : January 23, 1988

PRIMARY Five at Stronach School had been well-warned to behave themselves. At 2.30, one of Her Majesty's Inspectors was due to pay a visit to the class just to check that a country education still carries the cachet it has done for decades.

"Now, we're all going to be on our best behaviour, aren't we, boys and girls?" said teacher Miss Euphemia Pink, half-pleading.

A chorus of "Yes, miss" was peppered by "fairly that" and "michty aye", for country people are country people from the cradle on.

"And we know that the man who is coming to say hello to us is a very important man, don't we, boys and girls?"

The chorus was repeated. "And why is he very important, boys and girls?"

Stronach's diminutive eight-year-old hooligan, Wayne Spurtle, raised his hand, snapping his fingers like fury. "Please, miss! Please, miss! Because the teachers micht get the sack."

"Thank you, Wayne," said Miss Pink. "That will be quite enough from you for this morning, I think. And Sharon Grip, you really will have to stop daydreaming out of the window. The inspector of schools doesn't like little girls who daydream."

On the stroke of 2.30, the door opened and a burly little man was ushered in by a deferential headmaster. The stranger nodded to Miss Pink, who blushed and almost curtseyed, and strode to a desk at the back of the room.

Miss Pink called the class to order, reminded Sharon Grip not to daydream and began an arithmetic lesson. As the afternoon progressed, she became amazed by how well-behaved the class were and how they had seemingly metamorphosed into bright and intelligent young beings.

The inspector thought it too good to be true. At 3.15, he strode up to the front of the class to take over for a spell. He surveyed them for a few moments and the buzz of mild excitement died away to an expectant silence.

"Thank you," he said brusquely. "I don't particularly care for having to shout to make myself heard. I prefer that young people pay close attention in a classroom."

At that, Wayne yawned widely and loudly.

"You, lad," snapped the inspector. "Don't you go to bed early enough, or what is the problem?"

"I'm in ma bed ilky nicht at nine," said Wayne. "Bit I walkit three miles til the school this mornin fae ma grandma's hoose. Ma mither and me's bidin there lookin efter ma granda. He's tooken a bad turn."

"Tooken?" said the inspector. "Tooken? What on earth is wrong with your grammar?"

"There's nithing wrang wi ma grandma," said Wayne. "I telt ye. It's ma granda that's tooken the bad turn."

The inspector fixed Wayne with a hot stare. Wayne stared back blankly.

"So a three-mile walk has done this to you, has it?" said the inspector. "Three miles in the open air and you're half asleep. Sometimes I despair of the health of younger people these days. Don't you know that Winston Churchill was walking *ten* miles a day to school and thriving on it at your age?"

"And at your age he wis the prime minister," said Wayne.

The inspector stared a hot stare for a few moments, but said nothing.

Eventually, he began again. "Now, boys and girls," he said , quickly changing tack, "if I had ten oranges in one hand and seven oranges in the other, what would I have?"

"Affa big hands," said Wayne, and an excited buzz ran round the class. Miss Pink glowered at Wayne, but the inspector simply harumphed and carried on.

"You seem to be a bright young man," he said. "Tell me: suppose your father handed you a million pounds and you could do anything you want, what would you do?"

"I'd build a rocket an' tak a'b'dy in Stronach up til the moon for a picnic," said Wayne, sitting back and folding his arms.

The inspector was not entirely sure that Wayne was not poking fun at him. "Oh, come, come, come, now," he said. "You're just being silly."

"You started it," said Wayne.

This was too much for Miss Pink, and she jumped out of her seat and called to Wayne to remember his manners. For good measure, she shouted at Sharon Grip to stop daydreaming out of the window.

Miss Pink half bowed to the inspector and backed towards her seat. He continued. "Well, boys and girls," he said. "Perhaps you would like to ask me a question?"

There was a momentary silence until little Sharon Grip turned back from yet more daydreaming. "Please, sir, div ye like drivin yer funcy car?" The inspector smiled at the unusual question. "Why, yes," he said. "The Granada is a fine car. Why do you ask?"

Sharon turned to stare out of the window again and, as she turned, she said: "Because the scaffie's cairt has jist backit intil't."

The trouble with tourists

Episode 57 : September 3, 1988

THE American angler who had regaled Erchie Sotter with tales of his amorous exploits around the British Isles was now nearing the end of his sojourn at Stronach. He was cruising up the main street in his hired BMW, savouring the autumn sharpness in the air and the hint of winter to come.

As he slowed to let a combine-harvester lumber its way delicately round a parked car, he found himself pausing outside Stronach Emporium and General Stores.

As the combine shunted back and forth, with the driver growing ever more purple of face, the American's eyes lighted on shopkeeper Ebenezer Grip's pet cat.

There it sat, in the shallow sun, lapping milk contentedly from a small saucer. Fido was a fine cat (an odd name for a cat, mark you, but Ebenezer had always had a hankering after a dog).

But as fine a figure of a cat as Fido was, it was not the animal itself which caught the American's interest; it was the saucer containing the milk.

He peered at it, trying to make it out, and only a sharp shout from the combine driver of: "Hey, min! Shift yersel or I get by!" drew him back.

He manoeuvred past the combine and the parked car; drew into the side of the road, and walked back. He stood over Fido for a few moments while the cat shot him a superior, disdainful glance and carried on with her meal.

The American squatted down, ostensibly to pet and stroke the animal, but really to get a closer look at the saucer. "Lordy, lordy," he whispered to himself. "A sixteenth-century Montebello. Three thousand bucks if it's a penny."

As he tipped it up to get a closer look, a little of Fido's milk spilled from the opposite edge. Naturally a little disgruntled at the waste, Fido jabbed her claws into the man's wrist and drew them down the back of his hand.

The American jumped up in pain to find Ebenezer Grip standing in the shop doorway, watching him. He composed himself quickly. "Sure is one fine cat you got there," he said, rubbing his hand and fumbling for a hankie to stop the bleeding.

"Fido?" said Ebenezer. "She's nae bad. For a cat. Canna see the interest in cats masel. Selfish brutes o' things."

"Really?" said the American. "We're great cat-lovers in the States. Can't get enough of the dang things. Yes, sir, sure is a fine cat."

"I'll sell her til ye if ye like," said Ebenezer. "Gled ti see the back o' her. Clooks in a' ma furniture. Settee looks lik a Brillo pad. Costs a fortune in milk."

Sensing progress to his goal, the American feigned lack of interest for a few moments, and then gazed anew at the cat as if to convey how taken he was with her.

"Sure is one fine example of a feline," he said. "My family back home sure would like a Scotch cat like that." He paused. "OK," he said. "How much you want?"

"Fifty poun and she's yours," said Ebenezer, holding out his hand.

"Done," said the Yank, a little too eagerly. Before Ebenezer knew it, a crisp £50 note had been tucked into his overall pocket and the Yank had swept Fido into his arms and had turned to walk away. But he paused.

He turned back and hesitated. "Say," he said, "I'm sure you don't mind throwing in kitty's saucer, too. After all, she's used to it by now and it sure would be a shame to split them up when they look so fine together."

Rather presumptuously, he bent down to pick up the saucer.

"Na, na, na," said Ebenezer, covering the saucer with his foot. "I canna let ye hae the sasser. That's my lucky sasser, that. That's been wi me through the war. That's seen me through thick and thin. That's been in my femly for donkey's years and it's mair than ma life's worth ti pairt wi't. Ma mither's dyin words were: 'Look efter ma sasser.' Queer that, eh? It's the truth, though. 'Look efter ma sasser,' she said. And I swore on her dyin wish. It's sentimental value, ye ken. Ca me a soft aul thing, I suppose, bit there's memories there. And memories is memories, I'm sure ye'll agree.

"Ye ken something else? That's a sixteenth-century Montebello, that. They're worth a fortune.

"And ye ken something else? I've selt 23 cats this month."

57

Reunion fit for heroes

Episode 69 : February 18, 1989

THE salute was as sharp as ever it had been. Ebenezer Grip stood to proud attention in his living-room, surveying himself in the mirror.

The medals pinned to his chest told of a Service career of some merit. They were polished so brightly that when they caught the light and the reflection bounced off the mirror, Ebenezer had to turn away momentarily.

He shook his shoulders up and down once or twice to get his jacket to sit straight, picked a bit of fluff off one of his lapels and studied himself full-on and in profile.

"Ye're a fine-lookin figure o' a man," he mused.

The toot-toot of a car outside the shop led him to race through to the living-room to lift his mac off the back of the sofa. He walked through to the hall, took the door off the latch and stepped outside.

Sandy Brose and Walter Dreep were sitting in the car, beckoning Ebenezer to hurry up, so Ebenezer strolled across the pavement at a slower pace than usual and climbed into the back of the Escort.

Sandy pulled away from the kerb and the three chums were bound for Aberdeen and an RAF reunion at one of the city's top hotels.

"I see ye've yer medals on," said Walter as they sped past the end of the village.

"All present and correct," confirmed Ebenezer.

"That'll fair impress the guest of honour," said Sandy. "That'll pit his gas at a low peep."

"Fa's the guest of honour?" asked Ebenezer.

58

"Believe it or no," said Sandy, "it's some German air vice-marshal, ower fae Berlin. Bloomin funny choice o' a guest of honour at an RAF reunion if ye ask me."

"Bloomin funny," agreed Walter, smiling idly at the countryside passing by.

"That's nae trouble til lads lik us," said Ebenezer. "We've crackit Jerry's lugs afore noo. Let bygones be bygones, I say.

"I'm well experienced at handlin the big bugs, onywye. At the last reunion in 1979 there wis some Luftwaffy bummer ower fae Dusseldorf and I collared him in the lobby o' the hotel.

" 'Aye aye, Fritz,' I says, 'are ye likin yer spell in Scotland? Are we takkin good care o' ye?'

" 'Verr nice,' he says, 'verr verr nice.'

" 'Far is't that ye come fae?' I says. Well it turned oot he come fae Dusseldorf.

" 'Oh,' I says. 'A richt bonny place, Dusseldorf.'

"Well, that fair pleased him. His little chestie fair puffed up wi that. 'Haff you been to Dusseldorf?' he says, wi a kinna sneer on his face.

" 'Nivver,' I says, 'not a once. My son wis there, though.'

" 'Really?' says the Jerry. 'Ven vas your boy there?'

" 'Ivry nicht for fower wikks in 1942,' I says, 'he bombed hell oot o' the lot o' ye.'

"Funny thing. Great lads, the Jerries. Bonnie fechters. Nae sensa humour."

SANDY, Walter and Ebenezer were introduced to the RAF air vice-marshal at the dining-room door. In turn, he introduced them to his German colleague who clicked his heels and bowed subtly.

Ebenezer clicked his heels and bared his teeth. "I'm ninety-three," he said. "I wis in the first stramash that you lot startit. Royal Flying Corps. I'm still here. Ye didna finish *me* aff. I dinna finish aff that easy."

The German officer smiled politely, for the Doric had been so thick that he had understood not a word.

Eventually, Sandy, Walter and Ebenezer were installed at table and, after a moving welcome by the two officers, waiters began cruising round taking orders.

"Good evening, boys," said a rather effeminate and sibilant waiter whose chin almost scraped the tablecloth as he bowed. "My name is Justin and I will be your waiter for this evening."

"And we're yer customers," said Ebenezer, "so cut yer guff and get on wi't. Fit's on yer menu?"

The waiter was taken aback, but he composed himself to announce: "Well, we have a choice of two main courses. You can have choicest cuts of fresh Donside turkey, basted in a tarragon sauce with baby parsnips, sweetcorn, potatoes and relish with subtlest hint of spices of the Orient. Or there's mince."

"Mmmm," said Ebenezer, "well I'll tak a sup turkey, I think. Seein as how I wis a wing-commander, I'll hae a wing."

The waiter scribbled down the order and moved left to Sandy. "And for you, sir?"

"Well," said Sandy, "the turkey sounds tasty, richt enough. And seein as how I wis in the RAF band, I'll hae drumsticks."

The waiter then moved left to Walter who smiled emptily up at him.

"Well," said Walter, "the turkey certainly sounds richt tasty, bit I wis a rear-gunner.

"So I'll tak the mince."

Speechmaking spree

Episode 71: March 4, 1989

AFTER their successful outing to an RAF reunion in a top Aberdeen hotel, Ebenezer Grip, Sandy Brose and Walter Dreep were anxious to maintain the social momentum.

When Ebenezer announced he had been called to speak at the annual general meeting of the Grampian Speechmaking Society at a hotel at Inverurie, he invited Sandy and Walter to accompany him.

"Ye'll like it fine," he told them. "Intellectual stimulation's jist fit ye need. Especially you, Walter."

Walter had grinned emptily and nodded, although Sandy was a little more dubious. "I dinna ken aboot speechmakin," he said. "Sounds affa dry and dreary. Nae muckle pint til't, I dinna think. Naeb'dy's carin fit ye say, onywye. Is it nae affa toffee-nosed? A' big bugs and heid-bummers bumpin their gums aboot nithing ata? A lotta puffed-up naeb'dys?"

"Nithing o' the kine," snapped Ebenezer. "They're a' toppers o' lads. Jist toppers."

"I mean," said Sandy, "tak awa their funcy cars, their flash suits, their plummy accents, their money, their haircuts, their gold watches, their taste and their upbringin and fit hiv ye got? Jist fit *hiv* ye got?"

"Ye've got you twa," said Ebenezer. "Look, I ken ye're nae used til social occasions on this level, bit ye'll like it fine. And ye'll jist be in the audience. Ye winna hae nae spikkin yersels. Nae need for bein nervous at a big occasion. In fact, wi me bein on the committee, I'll pull a few strings and see if we can get ye in amon the first-timers, jist so's ye're nae overwhelmed wi sittin next til important folk at yer first visit. I ken fit it's like meetin a professor or a doctor for the first time. Ye're maybe nae up til that yet, so we'll start ye aff real easy."

"Of coorse, I canna sit wi ye this time," he explained, preening. "I'm at the top table for the vota thunks. I'll be up amon the doctors, solicitors, politicians, cooncillors, teachers, consultants . . . writers . . . doctors . . ." He paused while he thought a little more. "Doctors," he said. "Cooncillors . . . Hiv I said politicians?"

"Aye," said Sandy. "Ye've said them."

"Well," said Ebenezer briskly. "Onyb'dy that's onyb'dy'll be there. Ye'll pick me up at half-past six the morn's nicht. Dinna be late."

Ebenezer ushered Sandy and Walter out of his shop, slammed the door behind them, turned the OPEN sign to CLOSED and drew down the blind with a quick, sharp movement that belied his 93 years.

Sandy and Walter stood there for a moment or two until it dawned on them that they had been made responsible for transport.

"Hmm," said Walter as they began walking up the pavement for home. "Cooncillors, solicitors, politicians . . . Ye'd hiv thocht they'd hiv pickit someb'dy worth listenin til for a speechmakin society."

THE three chums turned up at Inverurie's top hotel to be met with a car park full of BMWs, Jags, Porsches and Mercedes. Sandy's A-registered Escort looked a little working-class in comparison.

"Now," hissed Ebenezer as he pulled himself out of the car, "ca this heap roon the back afore onyb'dy sees it and me thegither. I'm black affrontit." He shook his shoulders to get his new Crombie coat to settle properly.

He stepped into the lobby of the hotel and was met by the owner, who invited him to remove the coat. By this time, Walter and Sandy had returned from parking the car. Sandy handed his parka to the hotel-owner, and Walter offered his anorak.

"Far's yer pubbie, chiel?" inquired Sandy, clapping his hands together and rubbing them in anticipation.

Ebenezer quickly beamed an embarrassed smile at the hotel-owner, then pulled Sandy and Walter sharply to one side. "Pubbie?" he hissed. "Pubbie? This is nae a pub crawl, this. This is an important social event. Dinna you twa show me up here. This is a lotta important fowk and . . ." At that, Ebenezer spotted a familiar face.

"Giles!" he called. "Giles!" Sandy and Walter looked at each other.

"Hello, Giles! How are you? Sic a long time since I've seen you, ken. How is your charming wife? And your charming grandchildren? Real tomboys if I remember. Forever playing themsels in the dubs. Yes. Yes . . . No . . . No . . . Ebenezer. No, *Ebenezer* Grip. From Stronach. Stronach. Wee place up in the glen. In the howe. No, no. Ebenezer *Grip.*"

The two parted company and Ebenezer turned round to the inquisitive stares of Sandy and Walter. He coughed. "Close palla mine," he said, and marched on into the hall.

They sat down at table; Ebenezer making a great flourish of sitting down at the top table, beaming at the assembly and shuffling his speech notes prominently throughout the meal.

He was a little perturbed that the man on his immediate right seemed to have caught the eye of Sandy Brose and that the two were smiling and acknowledging each other at a distance. Sandy seemed to know a top-table person that he didn't. This top-table person couldn't be quite up to the standard expected of the Grampian Speechmaking Society if Sandy Brose numbered among his acquaintances. Ebenezer made a mental note to buttonhole the membership secretary to see if standards needed tightening.

The meal was delicious: elegant, beautifully cooked and presented. In fact, everything was progressing well until pudding came. It was chocolate mousse in a gingersnap basket. The mousse went down well but, at Ebenezer's first bite of the basket, there was a loud crack and he went deadly still and his face deathly white. He covered his mouth with a hankie and scanned the audience nervously. No one appeared to have noticed. It took a few seconds for the stranger on his right to lean towards him. "Can I help?" said the stranger. "Is something wrong?"

"Itsh ma top plate," slushed Ebenezer. "Itsh crackit in twa. Shplutten. And I've a shpeech ti mak in five minutesh."

The man thought for a moment. "Bend round the back for a minute," he whispered. Ebenezer did as he was told. The man hissed: "Quick, before anyone sees us. I've come straight from work. Try this out for size." Lo and behold, he pulled a top plate from his jacket pocket. Ebenezer did a quick swap. They fitted almost perfectly, give or take a bit of fluff or two.

Ebenezer thanked the man profusely then sat back upright, pushed the mousse basket to one side and prepared for his speech. When it came, it went down well. He sat down to good applause. Even Sandy and Walter had to concede that Ebenezer knew a thing or two about stirring an audience.

As they were going home that night, Ebenezer basked in the glow of glory.

"Aye, lads," he sighed, "us top-drawer lads fairly stick thegither. We fairly help each ither oot o' a ticht neuk. That dentist lad that wis sittin next til me, what a topper. An absolute topper! The lad you seemed ti ken, Sandy, that wis him. Fairly got me oot o' a ticht neuk."

"Fit dentist lad wis that?" said Sandy.

"Thon dentist lad that wis sittin next til me," said Ebenezer. "Thon lad ye wis lachin and smilin at a' nicht. The dentist."

"Fa? Bill?" said Sandy. "He's nae a dentist. He's an undertaker in the toon."

Wayne plays games

Episode 72 : March 11, 1989

ALTHOUGH just getting to the sensitive stage of her pregnancy – four months – Flo Spurtle shows no signs of letting up on the number of part-time jobs she does.

Home help, barmaid and cleaner are just some of the caps she has to wear because of her husband, Gibby, and his singular lack of success in obtaining gainful and permanent employment. Yet Flo never complains, even when she feels at death's door in the mornings.

When Flo's sister from Cornhill arrived for her fortnightly visit one Saturday afternoon, they sat in the kitchen for a fly cup and a buttery.

"How are ye feelin?" inquired her sister. "Still on yer feet day-in day-oot? Nivver a minute til yersel? That idle clort o' a man nae helpin?"

Flo stood up from the cupboard under the sink and straightened her aching back. She sighed.

"Ach, he's nae a bad aul stick, really," she said. "He's thochtfae in his ain wye. Last wikkend, we went intil the toon on the bus and we walkit past a flooer shop and he pintit oot a single reed rose in the windi. He telt me that if he hid the money, that wid hiv been the rose he wid hiv bocht me. What romantic." And she looked wistfully at the dirty dishes in the sink.

"Humph," said her sister, thoroughly unimpressed. "A single reed rose. A bittie corny, that, isn't it? That guff went oot wi timmer bilers."

"Och, it's fine, though," mooned Flo. "Maks ye think he cares, even though ye ken there's nithing in his heid bit open space."

"He nivver even *bocht* ye the rose," said Flo's sister. "He jist pintit it oot in a windi."

"Ach, weel," said Flo diffidently. "He looked affa disappintit that he couldna buy me a flooer, so I jist gave him the money."

Flo's sister sighed an exasperated sigh. "You're nae wise," she said. "Ye work yer knivs til the bone for spare change and ye gie it til that big idle clort for a flooer."

"Oh, bit he wis rare in the shop," said Flo. "He wis masterful. He jist stood there in the shop, dominatin ab'dy. He said: 'Excuse me. We need a seat. My wife's expeckin, ye ken.' He fairly timmered them in aboot.

"So this snooty-like wifie comes across. She says: 'What would sir like?' And Gibby says: 'I wid like one of yer finest single red roses, on its own, if you please. It's for ma wife. She's haein a baby.'

"So the wifie says: 'Certainly, sir. Would you like a box for it?'

"And Gibby says: 'No. We've got a second-hand pram.' " Flo's sister took another swig of coffee. "That's jist like him," she said.

At that moment, the front door clattered and there was a rush of footsteps into the living-room. Flo listened hard from the kitchen and was about to get up to check, but Wayne, her nine-year-old, shouted through: "It's only me! I've been playin wi Sharon Grip!"

"A'richt dearie," shouted Flo. "See and nae mak a mess ben there, the twa o' ye."

"No, we winna!" shouted Wayne. "We're awa up the stairs ti play Pregnant."

"OK, dearie," said Flo. "Jist be quaet aboot it." And there was a rumble of feet on the stairs and the slam of an upstairs door.

Flo settled down with another home-made buttery and idly spread it with syrup. She was about to start another line of conversation and looked up to see a rather concerned look on her sister's face.

"Fit's wrang?" she said.

"I dinna like til interfere," said her sister, "bit did you hear fit I heard? Did Wayne say he wis takkin one o' his little school pals up the stairs ti play Pregnant?"

"Oh, Lord," said Flo. She shoved the table to one side and raced out of the kitchen, through the living-room and up the stairs almost two at a time.

She flung open Wayne's bedroom door. Nothing. She flung open her own bedroom door. Nothing. Into the spare room. Still nothing. In a mild panic by this time, she tried the bathroom door. It was locked and, worse, there were giggles from inside.

"Wayne!" she shouted, hammering on the door. "Wayne! Come oota there this minute! Right now, young man, or yer faither'll hear aboot this fan he comes back fae the pub!"

A silence fell over the bathroom for a moment, and then there were sounds of movement. Presently, the bolt slid back and there was Wayne, soapy foam all over his face, and little Sharon kneeling on the floor next to the toilet.

"Fit like cantrips is a' this?" demanded Flo. "I've brocht ye up better nor this! Fit on earth d'ye think ye're up til?"

"I telt ye fit we were deein," said Wayne. "We were playin Pregnant. Weren't we, Sharon?" Sharon nodded her head briefly, without looking up.

"Pregnant?" said Flo. "Pregnant? Fit like a game's that?"

"Well," said Wayne. "I stan here shavin and singin and she spews in the lavvie."

Piercy's little problem

Episode 73 : March 18, 1989

ON ONE of their regular monthly shopping outings to Aberdeen, Virginia Huffie and Babbie Girn had been so trachled with bargains that they had actually missed their usual 4pm bus home from the Joint Station.

Virginia accepted this somewhat philosophically, but Babbie was irked to a considerably greater degree, for she knew that the next bus, at 5.30, would be packed to the gunnels and that her ample frame would be restricted.

"That's you and yer hakein aboot a' ower the place for nithing ata," she remonstrated with Virginia.

"We'll get packit in lik sardines a' the road hame. The bus'll be fulla big fat wifies wi message bags reemin ower; noisy kids bawlin and shoutin, and great big burly men pressin themsels against ye."

Virginia stopped in mid-chew, her dreamy smile growing ever wider. "Aye," she mused, "there's a lot ti be said for bus travel, isn't there?"

Presently, the bus drew up at its stance. The driver stood to change the destination board and Babbie barged her way through the assembling crowds until she and Virginia were at the front.

"Crack on, laddie," she called to the driver. "There's some o's wintin hame the nicht, nae the morn."

After a minor kerfuffle with a lanky student, Babbie bagged the front seat behind the driver; the better to get a full view of the road ahead and to survey every boarding and alighting passenger.

She had been right, though; the bus was certainly packed. All the seats were taken and the aisle was amply filled with standing passengers. At the last bus stop in the city, a gaggle of four frail pensioners boarded, obviously without a hope of getting a seat.

Babbie glowered at the lanky student on the other side of the passage, but to little effect. She tried a more pronounced glower, still to no effect. Eventually, so furious with the young man's lack of courtesy to the frail old women, she tapped him on the shoulder.

"I say, sonny," she said. "Far were you brocht up? Beirut? Hiv ye nae ony common decency? Did yer mither nae teach you *ony* manners? Self, self, self, that's a' you young folk think aboot nooadays. Lift yer great muckle backside oota there. You could stand up and let one o' this ladies hae a seat."

The young man was unimpressed. "And you could stand up and gie the hale lot o' them a seat," he said.

BY THE time the bus drew up outside Virginia and Babbie's terrace at Stronach, her mood had not mellowed. She made no comment, save for announcing that she was going home for peace and quiet. Virginia walked up her own garden path and disappeared inside her house.

Babbie had barely taken taken off her coat and switched on the kettle when a furious knocking got up at her front door.

"A' richt, a'richt," she called as she hirpled through to the front door again. "I'm comin. I'm comin."

She opened the door to be greeted with her travelling companion of just a few moments ago, but now in a highly distressed state.

"Fit's wrang?" asked Babbie. "Ye've nae been burgled, hiv ye? Ye've nae been took for fit little ye've got?"

"It's Piercy ma cat," sobbed Virginia. "There's something far wrang wi her. She's stiff as a boord in the kitchen. Myowin and greetin. Oh, Babbie, she's in sair pain. She's up the golden staircase this time, for sure."

"Calm doon," said Babbie. "I'll phone the vet and then I'll come back roon wi ye." And this she did.

THE vet noted Piercy's great discomfort as he felt her distended stomach. He examined her closely while Piercy's fellow cat, Big Black Sambo, a huge leering tomcat, sat idly in the easy chair by the fire.

"Well, Miss Huffie," said the vet, looking up. "I have good news for you. You're about to become a grandma. Piercy is expecting a happy event."

"Oh, that's nae possible, vetnery," said Virginia, aghast. "That's jist a non-starter. My Piercy's a good cat. She bides in the hoose a' day and she's nivver oot at nichts. She's jist nae that kinna cat, ye see. She's nae fit ye wid ca 'a good-time cat'."

"Well, Miss Huffie," said the vet, "short of immaculate conception, something romantic has happened to Piercy recently. Take my word for it." He spotted Big Black Sambo grinning on the easy chair at the fireside. "What about that tom cat over there?"

Virginia looked over at Sambo. "Fa?" she said. "Big Black Sambo? No, no, no, no, no. Nae Big Black Sambo. Not a chunce. Nae in this hoose, onywye."

"Well, it happens even in the best-ordered households, Miss Huffie," said the vet. "Believe me."

"Impossible," said Virginia. "Sambo's Piercy's brither."

Kate and the cookery contest

Episode 84 : June 3, 1989

SCHOOL open days have come late to Stronach. Away up in the howe, safe from the prying eyes of directors of education, Stronach Primary has ploughed its furrow quite happily for decades.

But a new headmaster last year introduced new techniques and Stronach Primary has been dragged into the 1970s. They expect to enter the 1980s by 1993.

Which is why, last Friday, the school's doors were thrown open as the good people of Stronach tramped through to see how their offspring are being prepared for life as useful Stronachers.

In Primary Five, a number of activity areas had been set up, and teacher Miss Euphemia Pink was keen to show off her pupils' culinary talents. Long before sex-equality arrived in Scotland's cities, Primary Five boys at Stronach were trying their hands at cooking and the girls were working with wood.

The policy has not gone down always terribly well with eight and nine-year-olds, but Miss Pink has gloried on regardless for nigh on 40 years.

To add piquancy to the open-day cookery competition, Miss Pink had invited Mrs Kate Barrington-Graham, incomer and chairperson of Stronach Community Council, to act as judge, with a £5 postal order as first prize.

Duly, the short-list of three finalists was waiting for her at 3pm, each standing behind his or her effort.

"Oh, no," hissed Wayne Spurtle to his two fellow competitors as Mrs Barrington-Graham appeared in the doorway. "It's that toffee wifie fae doon sooth. Her wi the bools in her mou. My dad canna be deein wi her. He says she bores her face intil a'thing. He says he disna understand a word she says."

"Your dad disna understand a word onyb'dy says," muttered Sharon Grip. And that line of conversation ended as Mrs Barrington-Graham, playing her role to the hilt, waved a regal wave at the assembled class.

With delicious disinterest, they simply stared back quizzically.

Mrs Barrington-Graham stepped forward to the line-up, smiled a toothy smile at the competitors, each of whom leered back at her as subtly as possible.

She cleared her throat and stepped forward to sample a morsel of the first candidate's fruit cake.

"Mmmm," she said, using her crannie to wipe a few stray crumbs from the corners of her mouth. "Dee-licious. Moist. Fruity. With just a hint of . . ."

"Gin?" suggested Wayne, and Mrs Barrington-Graham glowered at him.

". . . spices," she said, turning to the young cook. "You've obviously put a lot of effort into that my dear," she said.

"It come oot o' a packet," muttered Wayne, idly kicking his heels.

Mrs Barrington-Graham ignored him and proceeded to the next candidate, who was offering a selection of chocolate desserts. She tried a teaspoonful of the first.

"Mmmm," she said. "Dee-licious. What is this now?"

"It's chocolate mouse," said the candidate.

"Ha, ha, ha, ha," said Mrs Barrington-Graham, laughing just a little too loudly and in too affected a manner as she looked round to make sure everyone was watching her being condescending.

"No, no, my dear," she said. "You mean chocolate *mousse*."

"She kens fit she means," muttered Wayne.

Mrs Barrington-Graham glowered again and walked to Wayne and his iced queen cakes. She lifted one.

"Ye're nae stappin a' that in yer face at ae go?" he said.

"Look here," said Mrs Barrington-Graham, "you really are a most rude, rude, insolent little urchin. You're a disgrace to your family and the village." And she bit into the cake vigorously, as if to convey the degree of her displeasure.

She had wanted to be thoroughly dismissive of Wayne's efforts but, in fact, the little cake was delicious, and everyone in the class knew it was delicious, for they had already tried some and had been roundly impressed.

"Well," said Mrs Barrington-Graham, "you might be a cheeky little ragamuffin, but you can certainly cook, although how people like you manage it I just do not know. How did you manage to get such a smooth gloss on your icing?"

Wayne fixed her with steely eye.

"I lickit it."

Stronach:
two new stories

Sandy's black eye

The merry banter of children on their way to school woke Sandy Brose on Monday morning. He lay in a half-sleep as the shouts and laughs and cheers drifted up from the street below.

He lay for a moment while he came to himself, then turned on to his back and looked over to wish Geneva good morning. But the space where Geneva had been lying was empty. Not even warm. Geneva was long gone.

Sandy raised his head from the pillow to peer across at the alarm clock on Geneva's bedside table. And that was when the massive headache hit him. Like a blinding thump in the back of the neck, it tore through his head and tightened into knots behind his eyes. He collapsed back to the pillow.

"Michty," he said, wiping his brow and looking at the ceiling. "I surely hid a better nicht nor I thocht."

He lay for a few minutes more before making a second attempt. This time, he managed to sit himself up on the edge of the bed, but the pain lay heavily. His feet shuffled over the rug, searching for his slippers. Sandy scratched himself slowly once or twice and tried to lick his lips, but no wetness came. He was dry. Really dry.

Thankfully, all was quiet. The schoolchildren were past and he listened for any signs of life downstairs, but he heard none.

Sandy raised himself slowly and delicately (he thought once or twice that he might lose his balance, but he always recovered in time) then he shuffled towards the window. He raised his arms slowly, grasped the curtains and paused for a few minutes, summoning the strength to throw them back. When, eventually, he did, the bright April sun hit him at once and he stumbled back, blinking and cursing. He flopped back on to the bed, his eyes screwed tight against the blinding light.

It took fully five minutes before Sandy became sufficiently accustomed to the sunlight, the headache and the aches and pains in his joints before he felt able to shuffle over to the dressing-table for a good look at himself. And what he saw was not pretty.

Atop his stubbly chin hung a grey-yellow complexion, straggly hair lank with yesterday's Brylcreem, a nose which looked like someone had half-succeeded in twisting it off — and a magnificent, Technicolor black eye.

Sandy's jaw dropped. A black eye. A great big one. All the colours of the rainbow. He'd never seen one bigger, or more obvious or (ouch) sorer.

He stared at it for about a minute, taking it all in. It just looked back at him, seeming to grow bigger and blacker and brighter and sorer with every passing second. "She'll hae a Jamaica," he said to himself. "She'll tak a complete darker. Aff the deep end." He tottered to the door, opened it a crack and peered out. Nothing. Then he listened. Still nothing.

He scurried back to the end of the bed and put on his dressing-gown over his vest and pyjama trousers. "She telt me nae drinkin and nae fechtin," he mumbled. " 'Nae fechtin,' she said, 'or ye'll hear o't.' "

He opened the door slightly again, just to check the coast was still clear. Then, as quickly as the headache and his stiff joints would allow, he tiptoed along the landing — carefully avoiding the creaky floorboard outside the gloryhole — and, in a manoeuvre surprisingly deft for his age and condition, he nipped into the bathroom.

He looked again in the shaving mirror. At this side of the house, with the softer morning light and the blue decor, he fancied maybe the black eye wasn't so bad after all. After he had studied it for a few moments more, he decided he was kidding himself. This was a bosker. This was the Rolls-Royce of all black eyes. It could win prizes. And Geneva would certainly go mad.

"Maybe if I tidy masel up a bit, she winna notice," he said hopefully, as he reached for the tube of Ingram's Shaving Cream and his faithful brush. He had just finished soaping up his throat and chin when he heard the back door open and shut. He froze and listened hard.

The footsteps clicked across the kitchen tiles. He heard the kettle being filled. Then he heard the familiar squeak of the downstairs gloryhole being opened. Geneva must be hanging up her coat, he decided. He listened again, his hand and razor frozen in mid-air.

Then came a shout. "Sandy Brose! Are ye nae up yet!? Get up oota that bed this minute! There's grass doon here needin cuttin! If ye're nae up in five minutes, I'm comin up and kickin ye doon that stairs!"

"Comin, petal!" shouted Sandy quickly.

He looked at himself in the mirror again. Could he manage the next four or five days without letting his wife see the left side of his face? It would be difficult, he thought, but he could just about pull it off. He was a man of great resource and ingenuity, after all. He could do it.

He set about shaving. Each scrape made him wince. The rasp of the stubble seemed deafening, and he slowed as much as he could without cutting himself to ribbons. As he shaved, his mind raced frantically for solutions or, if need be, excuses. He wondered if a dab of his wife's foundation cream might do the trick. He thought he might smear his face with a few strategic smudges of soil, then she would think he had simply been working hard putting in tatties. But he knew she would only send him upstairs to wash.

Could he blame it on something else, he wondered? Could he have stood on a rake? Or walked into a lamppost? Or run into a door? No, he thought, quite properly; he really needed better excuses than those.

He was still gazing idly at the mirror, thinking, when he heard the footsteps at the top of the landing. Then the door opened. It was Geneva.

"Well, at least ye're up," she barked. "High time. Up near half the nicht boozin wi yer pals. Singin yer dirty songs. Tellin yer dirty stories. You get yersel doon that stairs in the next twa minutes or ye'll hear o't." And she closed the door.

All the time, Sandy had stared ahead at the mirror, pretending to shave, thankful that Geneva couldn't see the other side of his face.

When she had gone, he relaxed and slumped over the sink, grasping its edges, almost panting with relief. Then the door opened again. He snapped upright, knocking the shelf with his hand and sending a glass tumbler into the murky sinkwater. He pretended he was shaving again.

"And mind ye've seed tatties for collectin fae the fairm the day," she said. "The best o' the day's by already and ye've deen nithing. Nithing. Not a thing." She stood and watched, as if curious.

"Yes, yes, petal," said Sandy, fumbling for the tumbler in the sink without actually looking down and placing it back on the shelf. Geneva stood with her hands on her hips.

"And I hope ye're washin that tumbler afore ye're finished, Sandy Brose," she snapped. "I'm nae haein a fool tumbler in ma bathroom. Ye could catch onything aff a fool tumbler. Look at Virginia Huffie last year at the Daffodil Tea. She took a sup lemonade oot o' a fool tumbler. I telt her. I warned her. I said: 'That's a fool tumbler, that, Virginia.' Did she listen? Did she fiddle. Fit happened? Flat on her back for twa days wi a bug. That's fit fool tumblers dis for ye. Flat on yer back. You see ye wash that tumbler."

"I'll wash the tumbler, petal," stammered Sandy, still staring straight ahead.

Geneva made to close the door, but she stopped and looked again. Sandy didn't dare look back. Instead, he carried on staring widely at the mirror, shaving slowly, conscious all the while that his wife was looking in his direction.

She took a step towards him and every muscle in him tightened. The silence was unbearable. She was studying. He could tell she was studying by the way she was squinting and peering in his direction. A sweat broke on his brow, but he managed to carry on shaving as if nothing was happening.

"Sandy?" she said slowly. He whispered an inward prayer.

"Fit is't, petal?" he said.

"I dinna like fit I'm seein," she said.

"N-no?" he said. He paused, before summoning the courage to ask: "Fit is't that ye dinna like exactly?"

"Well," said Geneva. "Wid you say we're needin new curtains in this bathroom? That things we've got's lookin by their best, if ye ask me." She marched behind him and over to the bathroom window, where she took the curtains in her hands and felt and studied them.

Sandy, meanwhile, had to turn to keep his left eye away from Geneva. He stood now with his back to the sink and mirror.

"Aye," she said, letting the curtains fall to the window again. "It's a while since I've hid new curtains for ma bathroom. The wifie Dreep got new curtains for her bathroom just twa wikks syne. The dame doon at the drapery telt me. Horrible-lookin things, like, bit at least they're new. That things I've got's only fit for the ragbag."

She marched back in front of Sandy, who spun on his feet to keep his left side out of view.

Now she was back at the door and he was back facing the sink, hyperventilating with the stress of it all.

She stopped at the door again. "Ye'll get up that road for the tatties," she said. "Ye'll pit in a twa-three dreel. Then we'll hae a fly-denner and we'll awa intil the toon and see if we can get bonnie curtains for the bathroom." She watched, as if waiting for confirmation.

"Aye, aye, fairly that," said Sandy hurriedly, still shaving.

"Lord, Sandy," she said, closing the door. "Ye've deen mair shavin this mornin than the hale o' last wikk." She shut the door and began descending the stairs.

Sandy gripped the side of the sink again and sighed. He looked up at himself, a mass of nicks and blood spots and soapy lines — and that big black eye. He cupped his hands in the water and splashed his face two or three times before reaching for the towel hanging on the rail at the side of the sink.

"This'll maybe be a bittie mair difficult nor I thocht," he told his reflection, and he paused. He combed back his hair; the lank creemed strands above his ears came gradually into order again.

He rinsed the tumbler under the cold tap, dried it off on the towel he had used to wipe his face only seconds before, then let the water gurgle out of the sink. He didn't think to wipe the tidemark, for he was preoccupied with this, one of his tighter predicaments.

He tiptoed to the door, opened it a crack and listened. Geneva was clearly downstairs putting away groceries or some such. He stepped out on to the landing, closed the door behind him as softly as the old lock would allow, then he tiptoed back towards the bedroom, again avoiding the creaky floorboard beside the gloryhole.

He closed the bedroom door behind him and scuttled over to the dressing-table mirror, where he sat down and studied himself. He looked at himself square-on, in left profile, and in right profile. He squinted, opened his eyes wide, lowered his head and peered out from under his brows. No matter which way he looked, he could see at least some of the shiner.

He sighed. Then he sat and thought. He couldn't remember even raising his voice in anger, let alone the fight. It must have been a beauty, though. He hoped the other chap looked worse.

He dressed himself half-heartedly, gradually realising that, sooner or later, Geneva would have to be told and that he would have to steel himself for at least an afternoon's fury and then a long, heavy silence for possibly a week. Or maybe two. It wasn't as if he hadn't been told. She had said quite plainly before he left. "Nae drinkin a bucket. And nae fechtin." Clearly he had done both.

He wished he could remember more of the evening. He knew he had gone out to celebrate Erchie Sotter's birthday. He knew he had been seated at the same table in the bar with Walter Dreep and Fobbie Pluffer. He knew they had started a game of dominoes. And he could remember calling for his third round, which meant he must have had at least nine drinks. Then . . . it was all a blank.

Once dressed, he looked at himself in the mirror again, then turned to look round the room for any clues. Nothing. The room looked just as it always did. Geneva's side looked neat and tidy. His own side looked like a military band had marched through, scattering an Oxfam sale in its wake.

Then his eyes lighted on the telephone. Sandy looked at his watch. Walter would still be at home. Walter wasn't that much of a drinker. Maybe he could remember more of the evening. Maybe he could fill in the blanks.

Sandy strode across to the phone and sat down by the bed. "Wattie's ma boy," he said to himself . "He'll tell me. Aul chum. Aul pal." Sandy lifted the extension receiver as delicately as he could, to save it pinging down in the living-room. He listened to see if Geneva had been alerted, but there was no noise. He was sure she hadn't.

Sandy had dialled only two of the three numbers when the floorboard outside the gloryhole creaked. He threw the receiver back into its cradle, half-ran towards the wardrobe door, tugged it open and stood there, the door hiding his face.

Geneva marched into the bedroom. "Ye're nae still up here?" she demanded. "Lord, that grass is up anither inch. Will ye be muckle langer, or will I awa up til the fairm masel? Humphin bags o' tatties roon a fairm close, wi you back here still tooterin aboot lik a saft hen?"

"N-no, petal," said Sandy from behind the wardrobe door. "I'm jist lookin for ma cardigan. Ma workin cardie. I dinna like spilin a new cardie if I'm gairdenin."

"Ye ken fine yer workin cardie's on the back o' the gloryhole door doon the stairs," she said. She paused. Sandy waited for the worst. He stood staring wildly into the depths of the wardrobe, wondering what was to happen next.

"Ye hinna even made the bed, ye idle clort," she barked. "Half-past nine and nae a bed made nor a po teemed." With a long-suffering sigh, she stamped across to the bed, where she fluffed up the duvet and plumped up the pillows. Sandy waited until she had walked round to the other side, so that her back was to him, so he could leave without looking at her.

Then his moment came. "I'll awa and get ma cardie, than," he sang as he tripped out of the room and along the landing.

Sandy stumbled down the stairs two at a time, heart racing, brow rolling with sweat, eyes staring wildly. "I'll hae a heart attack," he thought. "A heart attack's fit I'll hae. This isna good for a body."

Sandy raced into the kitchen, pulled open the gloryhole door and hurriedly slipped his working cardie over his head. He heard Geneva coming down the stairs behind him, so he nipped smartly out the back door, where he stood for a few moments on the top step, wondering about his next move.

"Wattie," he said to himself. "I maun hae a news wi Wattie. He walked round the side of the house, being careful to turn away from the windows as he walked in front of them, then scuttled down the garden path and out into the street.

He surveyed the street for a few seconds, before deciding that he would probably manage to reach Walter's house without bumping into too many inquisitive villagers. As he walked, he held his head low and slightly to one side, lest prying eyes spied him from behind net curtains.

He paused behind the Dreeps' high hedge, wondering if he should risk the back door being answered by Aggie, or should he try the front, which was more likely to be answered by Walter? He stood and thought for a moment. Or should he throw stones up at a window? He'd seen them do that in films. But then he remembered Erchie Sotter's attempt to waken Virginia Huffie one morning several years before, and Virginia having to go to the doctor for stitches after the brick had landed on her leg.

"The phone," he thought, and he brightened almost at once. With another quick look up and down the street, he stepped out smartly for the phone box two streets away.

He managed to reach it with no great incident, pulled open the door, which was stiff through lack of use, and stood inside. He hadn't been in a phone box for years, so he read the instructions.

"What an affa price," he muttered. "Twa bob for a news."

He fumbled in his pockets, then — calamity. No change. Not a maik. He wailed in despair. And that was when he noticed Dorothy Birze peering in through the glass at the side of the phone booth, nose almost squashed flat against the scratched glass. Her jam-jar spectacles almost scraping the phone box.

"She's blin's a bat," he reminded himself. "She winna see a thing." He opened the door. "Hullo, Dorothy," he said brightly. She jumped back with a start. "Lord," she said, "what a scare ti gie a body. I didna ken there wis onyb'dy in there."

Sandy looked at his 15-stone bulk. "Aye, well," he mused. "I'm easy missed. Tell me, hiv ye ony change?"

"Not a bean," she said, smiling cheesily.

"Nae change?" he said.

"Not a bean. Nithing," she said again, looking surprisingly happy for someone apparently stony-broke.

"If ye've nae change," said Sandy, "fit wye were ye queuin at the phone box?"

"I wisna," she said.

"Ye were sut," said Sandy. "Ye were stannin there, waitin till I finished."

"I didna ken ye were in there," she said. "How could I hiv been queuin if I didna ken there wis onyb'dy there? I wis jist stannin here passin the time o' day. I often dee that. I hae a bit news wi folk queuin at the phone box, though I'm nae queuin masel. Onywye, I couldna hiv made a phone call."

"Fit wye?" said Sandy.

"Because I've nae change," said Dorothy.

Sandy stood and looked at her. She stood and tried to look back at him, although she wasn't quite sure where he was.

"Aye, well," he said. "I winna keep ye. I'm sure ye're busy."

"Nae really," she said.

"Well, *I* am," he said, growing more exasperated. "I've phone calls ti mak."

"Ye hinna nae change," said Dorothy.

"Well, I'll . . . I'll . . . "

"Ye could reverse the charges," said Dorothy.

"I'll . . . reverse the charges," said Sandy. "I'll reverse the charges. Now, I winna keep ye. You've things ti dee and I've charges ti reverse."

At last, Dorothy took the hint. She scooped up her vinyl message-bag, smiled a last cheesy smile at Sandy, turned and, with the words: "Cheerio, Bill" dancing in the April-morning air, scuttled off towards the centre of the village.

Sandy called the operator and asked for a transfer-charge call to Walter. It took a few seconds for the operator to connect. It took a few seconds more for the phone to be answered — by Aggie.

"Transfer the charges?" she barked. "Fae fa?"

"Caller, the party would like identification," said the operator.

"Tell her it's Mr Alexander Brose," said Sandy, growing increasingly impatient.

"Party, the caller is a Mr Alexander Brose," said the operator.

"Alexander Brose?" he could hear Aggie saying. "Alexander . . ? Fa? Sandy Brose? Sandy Brose is trying ti reverse the charges? Listen, lady, you tell Sandy Brose fae me that I'm nae peyin the phone calls o' a man that taks anither man hame in a state like he took my man hame in last nicht. Thon was a disgrace. And my Walter disna drink, that's the maddenin thing."

The phone clicked, buzzed and the line went dead. "I'm sorry, caller," said the operator, "the party appears to be unable to take the call."

"A'richt," said Sandy gloomily, and he put down the receiver.

He looked blankly at the inside of the phone box for a few moments more, wondering where to turn next. Presently, he looked up and down the street. A little knot of women with message-bags was gathered about two road-ends away, but they were far enough for him to escape without being noticed.

He heaved his weight against the inside of the door and emerged from the booth. A chill wind had got up in the last 15 minutes. With only his working cardie for protection, Sandy cursed his lack of foresight in not picking up his anorak, while he was at it.

He set out with bold step back the way he had come, noting that Babbie Girn appeared now to be finished battering her coconut mat against her front wall, and that Erchie's blinds were still drawn.

He was hurrying past Walter and Aggie's house when he saw Walter in his shed, trying to manoeuvre an old push mower out from behind a bike.

Sandy crossed the road quickly, stooping slightly to hide himself behind the Dreeps' hedge as best he could. He peeped up. Aggie was out on the back green, putting up the Monday wash, her stays blowing inelegantly in the breeze.

Sandy waited for a few minutes more, conscious of the curious stares of people in passing cars, so he began toying with the hedge shoots, pretending he was pruning or trimming or some such.

Soon, Aggie was back inside. Sandy peeped up above the hedge again. Walter had freed the mower and was replacing the bike in the shed. "Wattie!" he hissed. But Walter didn't hear.

Sandy ducked down for safety, looked up and down the street again, then peeped back up. "Wattie!" he hissed, slightly louder. Walter stopped for a few moments, then shrugged his shoulders and carried on rumbling about in the shed.

Eventually, Sandy stood up straight and said: "Wattie! Ower here!" Walter looked over and saw him. He extricated himself from the detritus in the shed, then strolled across, smacking his hands together to get rid of the worst of the dirt from his shed work.

"Lord, there's nae need ti shout," said Walter. "I've a hangover that wid split slate." Then he stopped. "Michty!" he gasped. "That's a richt keeker, that."

"Exactly," hissed Sandy. "Fit happened last nicht?"

"D'ye nae mind?" said Walter.

"Not a thing. The last I can mind is you chappin at a double-three at the doms, then . . ." Sandy shrugged his shoulders to show how lost he was. "Now I've a sair heid and an ee like a plate o' blackcurrants and custard."

"I dinna think I'll be muckle help til ye," said Walter. "I mind me chappin at the double-three . . . then it's a blunk." Walter looked up. "Well," he laughed. "Faivver it wis, Geneva'll seen sort them oot."

"Lord," hissed Sandy, "dinna even mention't. She disna even ken, and I darena let her find oot. D'you ken foo difficult it is keepin oot o' Geneva's road in a mornin?"

"I canna say's I div," said Walter.

"Well, it's nae easy," said Sandy. "She bores intil a'thing. I wis sweatin. I wis feart in ma ain hoose, and I dinna mind admittin't."

Then Walter's eyes grew wide and he almost pushed Sandy to one side. He had seen Geneva stamping down the street, jaw set, eyes afire. "Awa!" he hissed to Sandy. "Awa afore it's ower late!" On trust, Sandy headed for the side of the house.

Just as Sandy cleared the rose bed in the front garden and scuttled down the side of the house, Geneva stopped at the other side of the hedge and peered over. She studied the scene for a few seconds, before asking the obvious question. "Far is he?" she said quietly.

"Fa?" said Walter.

"King Farouk," she said. "The Good-Time Boy. Ma man! SANDY! Far is he?"

"Is he nae wi you?" said Walter.

"Dinna be funny," snapped Geneva. She took a few steps back up the street, then burst through the garden gate, evidently determined to track down her man. She stopped beside Walter. "We can mak this easy, or we can mak it difficult," she said. "Sandy kens he his seed tatties for collectin fae the fairm. Instead, he's oot haein a good time. I ken him. If there wis an Olympics for idlin aboot deein nithing, Sandy Brose wid win the Gold. Now, far is he?"

An involuntary glance to the side gave the only clue Geneva needed. She looked up towards the side of the house, then rolled up her sleeves. "Right," she said. "Thank you, Walter. I'll sort this oot masel."

Having made his escape, Sandy had crept round the side of the house, down the back garden, along the front of Walter's greenhouses and up the side of the coalshed, intending to secrete his 15-stone bulk behind the substantial, granite-built shed-cum-bunker.

Unfortunately, it was that very 15-stone bulk which prevented him from moving as lithely as was necessary in the circumstances. Just as Geneva reached the back of the house, she saw Sandy dipping in behind the coalshed.

She smiled a confident, determined smile to herself and then strode out. As she drew closer, she pressed herself back against the wall of the coalshed, intending to step out sharply and catch him.

As she reached her side of the corner, she paused. Just inches away, at his side of the same corner, Sandy had had the same idea.

Husband and wife, unaware of each other's presence, peered slowly round the corner — and their eyes met. Sandy's eyes widened. Geneva's eyes narrowed.

"Hullo, petal," said Sandy, that familiar white flash of panic running through him. Then, suddenly, he remembered the black eye and tried sharply to turn away to hide his left side. His nose battered into the sharp corner of the granite, tearing the skin in scrapes and tatters, and he howled with pain.

"Aye," crowed Geneva, "that's the price o' ye. Ye great boozin waster."

But Sandy was weary. The battle was finished. He stood meekly, holding his stinging nose, unable to bear the strain of his deceit any longer. Slowly, he turned to face Geneva squarely, the black eye rich with colour and depth and spread.

Her tirade continued. "I'd be better aff wi a cat nor you," she snapped. "Ye get intelligence fae a cat. Lord, I'd be better aff wi a budgie nor you. I hinna met sic an eeseless object as you in a' ma born days!"

"I'm sorry, petal," whined Sandy. "I dinna ken fit came ower me."

Geneva stood, arms akimbo, bearing a fury unlike any fury she had borne before. Sandy fancied she looked like she might hit him at any moment, so choked was she with rage.

"As for the drinkin last nicht," he said meekly, "well, I'm sorry. I jist got cairried awa. I ken ye telt me. I ken ye said nae drinkin. It wis jist in the heat o' the moment. Ye ken fit like."

But Geneva glowered the glower of a million hot coals. Evidently, she did not ken fit like. She had little conception fit like, it seemed.

"And as for the fechtin," continued Sandy.

"The fechtin?" said Geneva.

"Well," said Sandy, "ye can see I wis fechtin, can't ye?" And he stood a little closer and pushed his face closer to hers, as if she might have missed the black eye. "I ken ye said nae fechtin. Bit, believe me, I canna mind fechtin ata. I ken I must've. I jist canna mind it. I'm a disgrace, I ken, gettin that drunk that I canna mind nithing, bit that's it. I've nae excuse. Someb'dy battered me."

"Someb'dy battered ye," agreed Geneva. "Are ye surprised? Ye came hame roarin fu, singin yer dirty songs this mornin. Bangin on the door. Tappin on the windies. Gettin folk oot o' their beds.

"I battered ye!"

The Englishman, the Scotsman and the American

The big clock on the wall of the Stronach Arms ticked away the seconds slowly, steadily. The huge hand slipped past another minute with a dull clunk and Erchie looked up from his half-pint.

He checked his watch and noted it was a few minutes slow. Then he sighed slowly and looked into the golden stain at the bottom of his glass. Pickings had been thin today, indeed. Tourists, those fine souls of such gullibility and generosity, had been few and far between. Even the locals hadn't turned out in such numbers. So Erchie had had to take the unusual step of buying his own half-pint. Things had come to a pretty pass.

"Affa quaet, John," he said to the barman, who was standing behind the bar idly polishing glasses which were already perfectly well-polished.

"Quaet," confirmed John. "It'll maybe pick up as the evenin weers on. Affa weather, though."

And Erchie nodded in agreement. He looked out at the gathering clouds. Not even the hardiest Stronach soul would venture out on such an October night of stormy blast and driving rain.

"Are ye for anither half?" asked John.

"Na, na," said Erchie, lifting the glass for a mouthful of lager which really wasn't there. "I'll hud on a coupla minties yet. I'll maybe hae some company afore lang. It surely canna bide this quaet a' nicht." And John smiled to himself, for he knew Erchie too well.

Erchie gazed wistfully up at the wall clock again. It bore the legend GNSR which, as every schoolboy in the North of Scotland knows, stood for Great North of Scotland Railway. The clock had been bought from the old Stronach railway station in 1965, two days after the Beeching cuts closed the line for good; two days after Erchie did his last run as engine driver.

Erchie smiled wistfully and sighed again. "That clock's seen an affa history, John," he said. "So ye keep tellin us," said John.

"Aye," said Erchie. "Yon's a historic clock, yon. Think o' a' the folk that's seen that clock. Think o' a' the journeys that's startit wi a look at that clock in the station waitin-room. Think o' a' the hopes and the fears that clock witnessed in a hunder year. Think o' the sojers gaun aff til the wars. And think o' them comin hame. Think o' the lads that didna come hame. The last thing they saw in their hame soil wis that clockie."

"Ye're affa doon aboot the mou the nicht," said John. "That's affa depressin conversation, that. Hiv ye nae jokes?"

"Jokes?" said Erchie. "Jokes? Fit is there for lachin at on a nicht lik this? It's rainin. There's a gale. Ma hoose is caul. And I've nae company on a nicht oot. And now ye're needin jokes."

Out in the car park, an engine revved as a car pulled off the main road. The lights brightened the bar windows for a few moments, then the engine died and the lights went out. Erchie rose and strolled across to the bar with his empty glass.

"Stand by for action, John," he said. "I think we've got visitors."

It took a few moments for the double doors to open. When they did, the noise of the storm outside grew louder, then died away as two men closed the doors behind them. Then the inner doors opened and Erchie and John saw two men, both dressed quite casually, although obviously expensively.

Both were tall, at least six-feet-three, although one was much broader than the other. They slipped off their Burberry overcoats and shook them to get rid of excess rain, then the thinner of the two carried both macs to the coatstand, then carried on to the toilet. The broader one approached the bar, running a hand through his windswept grey hair, smoothing it down.

"Evenin!" he said cheerily, with a boom which told immediately that he was American. "Nice weather you got here."

"Gaun ye're a dyeuck," said Erchie.

"Beg pardon, sir?" said the American, leaning forward slightly as if mild deafness had afflicted him.

"Gaun ye're a dyeuck," repeated Erchie. "Nice weather gaun ye're a dyeuck." But the American looked just as mystified. "It's nice weather," explained Erchie, "*if -you're - a - duck.*"

"Right," said the American, obviously glad that that little point had been cleared up. He turned to John.

"Barkeep," he said heartily. "This here American needs a little something to warm up my insides on a cold, cold Scottish night. What you got?"

"Now here's far I can advise ye," interrupted Erchie. "Ye canna beat local knowledge on an important matter lik this. Insider knowledge, as ye micht say."

The American nodded cagily. "Sure, sure," he said slowly. "So what do you recommend?"

"Fit div I recommend?" said Erchie. "Fit div I recommend? Well, of coorse, for a fine gentleman lik yersel; a gentleman wi obvious good taste that disna mind spendin his siller on the gweed things in life; that looks for the very best in a'thing . . . I wid let ye try a malt whisky."

"Sounds dandy," said the American. "Bartender, gimme a malt whisky."

"Ye canna order a malt that wye," said Erchie, chastising mildly. "There's malts and there's malts. Now, I wid try a Glenfiddich, a Glenmorangie, a Glengarioch or The Macallan."

"Gee," said the American, rubbing his chin, "that's quite a choice."

"Exactly," said Erchie, "and that's why I'm here ti help ye. We'll hae a tastin session. I'll seen learn ye aboot malts. Ye'll be in big demand back in America efter this. John, set up twa Glenfiddichs, Glenmorangies, Glengariochs and Macallans."

John looked at the American, and the American shrugged his shoulders as if to say: "Why not?" John turned to the bottles of malt on the shelf behind the optics, and while Erchie looked eagerly at the bottles, the American reached into his back pocket.

Just then, the second stranger emerged from the toilets corridor and walked slowly towards the bar.

"Jim!" said the American. "What'll you have?"

"A G and T, if I may," said the very English gentleman.

"And a gin-tonic, bartender," said the American, pulling a £20 note from his ample wallet and laying it on the bar. The wallet's fullness did not go unnoticed by Erchie.

"Erchibald Sotter," said Erchie, beaming, to the American, offering the international hand

of friendship.

The American took the hand and gave it a hearty shake. "Carl Bodnar the Third," he boomed. "Mighty fine to meet you, sir."

"Erchibald Sotter," said Erchie, offering his hand to the Englishman, who took it a little less eagerly and shook it considerably less enthusiastically, and said without looking at Erchie: "Indeed. James Wilmington."

Erchie smiled pointedly, waiting for the Englishman to look at him and return the compliment, but it didn't come. Instead, the Englishman watched intently as John the Barman poured the gin and tonic, took it, turned his back slightly on Erchie and raised his glass to the American and said: "Down the hatch."

The Englishman smacked his lips at the fIrt sip of his G and T then looked at the array of whiskies on the bar in front of the American. "You're terribly thirsty," he said with a half-smile.

"This gentleman here has kindly offered to advise me on the delights of Scotch whisky, Jim," said the American. "Imagine that. My own personal tutor. Wait till they here about this back in the States."

"Hmm," said the Englishman, evidently unimpressed.

"OK, Mr Sotter," said the American. "Go to it."

Erchie lifted the Glenfiddich and took a hearty sip. He made a great palaver of swilling it round, looking as if he was savouring the bouquet, the subtle nuances of flavour and the smoothness on the tongue. Then he swallowed.

"And that," he said, "is a Glenfiddich."

"Not terribly difficult considering the barman has put the bottle next to the glass," said the Englishman, taking another sip of his G and T. "In fact, some people might suppose that this game is a handy way of getting a free drink. You know what Scots are like. Anything for nothing."

"Now, Jim," said the American, mildly upset at the discourteous behaviour of his companion.

"It's a'richt," said Erchie, raising a cautionary hand. "We're used til this." He turned to the Englishman. "Now, Mr . . . Wilmington, did ye say yer name wis? Now, Mr Wilmington, fit's rattled your cage? Say yer piece."

"Just what I said," said Mr Wilmington. "Scots are famous for trying to cadge anything and everything at the expense of other people. They're famous the world over for their meanness. Haven't you heard the story of the Aberdonian who spotted a sixpence in a London street and leaped out to grab it and was run over by a taxi? The coroner's verdict was Death Through Natural Causes." And he smirked a satisfied smirk as he took another sip of his G and T.

"Weel, weel," said Erchie. "Somebody surely came by the smiddy the day."

"What's that?" said the American, grinning.

"Came by the smiddy," repeated Erchie. "Passed the blacksmith. Got their wits sharpened up."

"Say, that's a good one," said the American, and he slapped his thigh.

"Och, I've better nor that," said Erchie. "Fit aboot the Scotsman whose faither died and he'd ti send a telegram til his brither in London. He went intil the post office and he wrote oot: 'Father dead. Funeral on Thursday.'

" 'Now Mr MacDonald,' said the post-office wifie. 'Ye get *ten* words for sixpence.' Well, the Scotsman wis sair puzzled and he went aff til the little deskie at the back o' the post office and he thocht and he thocht. Then the post-office wifie saw him writin lik his life dependit on't and then he came back til the coonter and gave her the bittie o' paper again. And she read:

" 'Father dead. Funeral on Thursday. Six, seven, eight, nine, ten.' "

The American threw his head back and laughed. "That's a good one," he said. "I'll have to remember that one for the folks back home."

"Better nor that," said Erchie, "fit aboot the little lassie collectin for the Kirk? She went roon the doors in Aiberdeen wi her little tinnie and she came til this door in Crown Street. She chappit at the door and she waitit a coupla minutes, then this aul, aul mannie shuffled til the door and he opened it.

" 'Aye?' he said.

" 'I'm collectin for the Kirk,' said the lassie. 'Hiv ye a few pennies ye could spare for the Lord?'

"Well, he reached oot and he took the tinnie aff her and he wis closin the door and he said: 'I'll jist tak yer tinnie. I'll be seein the Lord lang afore you.' "

The American laughed anew. He threw his head back and laughed loud and long. Erchie took a satisfied sip of his own Glenfiddich and smiled, while Mr Wilmington simply stood coldly and stared.

The American tugged a hankie from his pocket and wiped the tears from his eyes. Through his bleary vision, he looked at Mr Wilmington. "Jim," he wheezed, "you want another gin-tonic?"

"No, thank you," said Mr Wilmington curtly. "One is sufficient at the moment." He stood and was obviously thinking, then he said:

"Of course, you know that Scots parents won't buy their children ice-cream because it's cheaper to tell them ghost stories and have their blood run cold."

"Is that right?" said Erchie. "Well, well, well." He turned to the American and said: "Are ye ready for yer Glenmorangie, noo, Mr Bodnar the Third?"

"Call me Carl," said the American slapping Erchie on the back. "And let's take these drinks over to the comfortable seats in the corner." And so the party removed itself to the seats in a little alcove at the back corner of the lounge.

Erchie took a sip of the Glenmorangie. He savoured it, swilled it over his tongue then swallowed it with a satisfied smack of his lips. "And that's a Glenmorangie. Rhymes wi orangey," he said. While the American tried his own Glenmorangie, Erchie announced:

"An Aberdonian in London sent a letter hame til his folks and he wrote: 'PS. If there's nae a stamp on the envelope, it fell aff in the post.' "

Carl laughed loudly again. He could barely hold his whisky, and he put it down on the table in case he spilled it. Mr Wilmington, meanwhile, simply sat and looked at his drink.

"This is a real fine malt whisky, Erchie," said Carl, swilling the Glenmorangie on his tongue. "Real fine. I'm a bourbon man myself, but this beats all."

"Fine pleased ye like it," said Erchie. "And did ye hear aboot the Scotsman that bocht twa raffle tickets and he won a car and he sat doon greetin?

"A wifie came ower til him and she says: 'Mercy, Wullie. Ye've jist won a spleet-new car. Fit wye are ye greetin? Are ye overcome wi emotion?'

" 'No,' sobs Wullie. 'Ae ticket wid hiv been enough.' "

Carl roared again, and tugged his now well-damp hankie from his pocket, while Erchie swigged the last of his own Glenmorangie.

"Do you know why Aberdonians tell their children funny stories?," said Mr Wilmington. "It makes them happy in their old age. That's how long it takes the joke to dawn on them."

Erchie and Carl looked at Mr Wilmington and then at each other.

Erchie countered with: "And fit aboot the Aiberdonian that lay ill and he wisna expectit ti laist lang? And a little candle flickered aside his bed.

"His wife sat and sat and sat wi him, bit she needed groceries so she got up and she put on her coatie and she says: 'Now, Dodie, I winna be lang. Bit if ye feel yersel slippin, mind and blaw oot the candle."

Carl was now beside himself. He was laughing so heartily he was holding his sides for the ache of it. Erchie had never had such an appreciative (or generous) audience and he felt obliged to offer his money's worth.

"Fan the wife came back fae deein the messages, she went intil the kitchen and it wisna lang afore Dodie smelled the smell o' hame bakin fae doon the stairs.

" 'Mima!' he shouted doon the stairs. 'Mima! Is that hame bakin? I could manage a bittie shortbreid, I think.'

" 'Ye'll dee nithing o' the kind,' shouts Mima up the stairs. 'That's for the funeral!' "

Carl actually stood up this time, tears streaming from his eyes and his handkerchief doing little to help. "You Scotch," he said, wheezing with laughter. "You sure know the funny stories. And you know what I like about you? You sure know how to laugh at yourselves!"

Wilmington shot Erchie a withering glance. Carl went off to the toilet, still laughing and muttering: "That's for the funeral! Hot dang!"

The atmosphere cooled markedly when the door to the toilets corridor swung shut. Erchie looked expectantly at the remaining two glasses of malt, while Mr Wilmington sat, legs crossed, and looked around him at the empty lounge.

Presently, Carl reappeared and sat own with a flourish at the table. "Now, Erchie," he said. "You're gonna have to slow up on the stories. I ain't sure my constitution can cope with too much hilarity in one night. My doctor tells me to take it easy, so I came on vacation to Scotland. Lord, I've done more exercise and now more laughing in a week here than I do in a year back home. So just you take it easy, huh?"

"Fitivver you say, Mr Bodnar the Third."

Carl smiled and looked at the two remaining whiskies. "Now, what is this next one?"

"That's a Glengarioch," said Erchie confidently. "Ye'll like it. They growe tomatas in the distillery."

"Say," mused Carl, lifting the glass and admiring its colour. "A tomato-flavoured whisky. They'll never believe this back home."

"Nae tomata-flavoured," said Erchie. "They jist growe tomatas in greenhooses so's nae ti waste a' the spare heat fae the distillery. Richt fine tomatas, tee."

This time, Carl swigged first and swilled it around gently, then swallowed. "Mighty fine," he boomed. "Mighty, mighty fine."

"We were passing a boarding house in Aberdeen this morning," said Mr Wilmington with a suddenness that made Carl and Erchie look round at him.

"Yes," he continued, "and one landlady had a sign in her window: 'Lodgers Taken In.' And I thought to myself: 'How true.' "

He sat back and waited for reaction, but none came. Erchie and Carl looked at him, mystified, for a few moments, then Erchie said: "Bit hiv ye heard aboot the Englishman, the Irishman and the Scotsman adrift on a little raftie in the Atlantic? The Englishman got doon on his knees and prayed. The Irishman got doon on his knees and prayed. The Scotsman threw himsel ower the side. He thocht there wis gaun ti be a collection."

Carl laughed again.

"Or fit aboot the lad that went intil a corner shoppie in the toon and he bocht twinty fags and left withoot pickin up his change? The grocer tried catching his attention. He tapped and tapped and tapped on the windi. Wi a duster."

Carl laughed louder.

"And fit aboot the young Scotsman? His wife hid triplets and he wis really annoyed because he'd ti buy ae feedin bottle."

Carl's shoulders heaved again and the tears were streaming down his face as freely as they had at the beginning of the evening.

"I tell you," he said. "I'm really enjoying myself. Especially since my doctor is Scotch. Wait till I get back home and tell him all these stories. He'll die laughing."

Carl and Erchie took another swig of their whiskies. Mr Wilmington, meanwhile, sat stony-faced. He had finished his gin and tonic, but had steadfastly refused another.

"By the way," said Carl. "You Scotch, you really make great doctors."

"I've heard that," said Erchie. "Great doctors, great engineers and bonnie fechters, that's us."

"No," said Carl. "I mean, really great doctors. My Scotch doctor told me he'd have me walking around within a week. He was absolutely right. I had to sell my car to pay his bill!"

This time, it was Erchie's turn to laugh uproariously. Carl laughed loudly at his own joke and slapped Erchie on the back in all the revelry. Mr Wilmington, meanwhile, managed a wan smile out of courtesy to his companion.

Carl, rubbed his eyes with his hankie, then looked down at the remaining whisky. "Lord, Erchie," he said. "I'm having me some of the finest, most expensive Scotch malt whiskies I'm ever likely to have. My doctor would have a fit."

"Fit wye's that?" inquired Erchie, suddenly concerned. "Are ye on a diet?"

"Nope," said Carl. "I still owe him a thousand dollars!"

Erchie laughed again, and Carl went on: "I went back to him just before I left to come to Scotland and I said: 'Look, doc, I'm having pains in my heart. What do I do?'

"He says to me: 'Carl,' he says. 'The best thing for you is to stop eating so many fatty foods, give up alcohol and stop smoking.'

" 'OK, doc,' I says, 'to be honest, I don't deserve the best. What's second-best?' "

And the two men burst out laughing anew. Even John the Barman, who was stone sober, found all the laughter infectious and was grinning to himself at the far corner of the lounge.

It took Carl and Erchie a few moments to calm down but, when they did, Erchie said: "I went til the village doctor here. He gave me some peels and he telt me I hid ti tak a peel wi a little drappie whisky ivry nicht afore ma bed.

"Well, I went back a fortnicht later because I still didna feel ony better, and the doctor said: 'Are you doing what I told you to do? Are you taking a pill with a little whisky every night before you go to bed?'

"And I says: 'Yes, doctor. I am that. I'll admit I've fa'n a wee bittie ahen on the peels, bit I'm three month in front wi the whisky.' "

Carl roared again and slapped Erchie on the back so hard that Erchie was almost pitched across the table. Mr Wilmington looked disapprovingly on all the hilarity and looked pointedly at his watch, but the American was having too good a time to notice.

"So, Erchie, my boy, what's this last whisky you got for me?"

"This is The Macallan," said Erchie, "said by many connoissewers – and ither folk that kens a lot aboot whisky – to be the Rolls-Royce of whiskies. Smooth as a baby's bottom, bit a lot tastier." He lifted the whisky to his lips and sniffed deeply. The roll of his eyes told of his rapture.

Carl did the same, and his delight was instant. "Lordy, lordy," he intoned. "Such a neat aroma. Such an inviting bouquet, you might say."

"Ye micht say that, indeed, Carl," said Erchie. "It's a rare whisky, that's richt enough."

"By the by, did ye hear aboot the great excitement on Deeside? A laddie had tummled aff a brig and fa'n in the Dee. This big strappin chiel comes by and he sees a' the commotion so he dives in and he saves the laddie.

"Well, things got calmed doon and the hero wis approached by the laddie's faither. 'Are you the man that saved my loon?'

"Well, the lad wis bashful, bit he says: 'I am.'

" 'Fine,' said the faither. 'Far's his bunnet?' "

Carl was about to start roaring with laughter again, but Mr Wilmington butted in first.

"Oh, for goodness sake!" he said. "All we hear about is jokes, jokes, jokes. All these funny stories about the Scots. I'm sick fed up with it all. Scots, Scots, Scots. That's all we've heard about all evening. Aren't you fed up with it, Carl?"

But Carl was plainly not fed up with it at all. "Jim," he said. "All evenin, you've had a face like a coyote chewin a lemon. Lighten up, man. You're on vacation."

"Lighten up?" snorted Mr Wilmington. "Lighten up? With this professional old yokel telling funny stories and wheedling free whisky out of you all evening? I'm fed up hearing funny stories about the Scots. In fact, I'm fed up hearing about the Scots. Lord, why can't we have a funny story about the English once in a while?"

"Aweel," drawled Erchie, taking a slow slip of his whisky. "We'd fairly tell a funny story aboot the English, bit far's the fun in that? My mither aye said: 'Dinna mak fun o' the disadvantaged.' "

Stronach:
the
recipes

"They're really a friendly lot at Stronach, you know. Mrs Barrington-Graham up at Bridge House says she really can't abide the villagers, but I always find people treat you as you treat them, and I couldn't wish for better neighbours.

When we threw a party for Tom's christening, we invited all the locals, and this was the dish they all raved about, so I thought I might as well share it with you.

It looks very complicated, and I suppose it is a bit fiddly, but I think it's worth the extra effort. You can use fresh salmon if you want a really Rolls-Royce dish, but I find tinned salmon much more economical and, to be honest, a little tastier. Be sure it's not too wet; that's the only warning I'd offer. Drain as much as you can out of it.

The beauty of Salmon Wellington is that you can serve it cold with a salad, or hot with potatoes or rice, and vegetables. It tastes equally good, although I have a sneaking preference for it hot on a cold winter's day.

You can make your own puff pastry. I think Mrs Brose and Mrs Dreep were horrified when I told them I'd just bought a slab of ready-made from the butcher but, really, I don't think they could have told the difference if I hadn't let the cat out of the bag.

Be sure you glaze it thoroughly with beaten egg. It's tempting to economise and just use creamy milk, but egg is essential. And be sure you cover all of it, or it will dry out."

Claire Macfarlane's
SALMON WELLINGTON

Ingredients
439g (15.5oz) tin red or pink salmon
50g (2oz) butter
50g (2oz) plain flour
1 tbsp oil
4 tbsp freshly chopped parsley
Salt and freshly ground black pepper
100g (4oz) mushrooms, sliced
4 spring onions, trimmed and sliced
675g (1lb 5oz) ready-made puff pastry
1 Size 3 egg, beaten, to glaze

Oven
190C 375F Gas 5

1. Preheat oven. Lightly oil baking sheets.

2. Drain the salmon, pouring the juice into a measuring jug. Make up to 200ml (7fl oz) with cold water.

3. Melt butter in a pan. Stir in the flour and cook for one minute. Remove from the heat and add the juice mixture. Bring to the boil, stirring constantly, until thickened. Add the parsley, salt and pepper, mushrooms and spring onions into the sauce and set aside.

4. Divide the pastry into six, then roll out each piece on a lightly floured surface to a rectangle 20x15cm (8x6in).

5. Flake the salmon before laying it down the centre of each rectangle. Top with the sauce.

6. Brush the edges of the pastry with beaten egg and bring them up over the salmon filling, sealing together firmly.

7. Trim. Brush with beaten egg. Decorate with salmon pastry shapes made from the pastry trimmings. Brush with egg. Bake for 20-25 minutes until pastry is golden.

" The really difficult thing about producing cuisine of this standard once we arrived in this village was finding the correct ingredients. That little man at the village shop hadn't even *heard* of Grand Marnier. He thought it was some sort of French gun in World War 1. As for Tarragon, he insisted it was a town in Spain and that his grandchildren had been there for their holidays in 1978. Isn't it just too, too dreadful?

However, I now have my own herb bed up at Bridge House, so that has solved the problems of fresh-herb supply. Don't be tempted to do without the tarragon, for it adds a certain je-ne-sais-quoi and really accentuates the flavour of the chicken and the sauce. It also looks nice, although Godfrey refers to it as 'the weeds'. Isn't he a pet?

This recipe really is frightfully quick. I find that if I set out all the ingredients in bowls before we go to theatre in Aberdeen or a recital at Haddo, I can just whizz through the preparation in barely fifteen minutes when we bring guests back for a post-theatre supper. In fact, we've hardly got time to quaff our aperitifs before the buzzer on the Aga's ringing away merrily.

You can use lemons if you're feeling sadistic, but we find that oranges give the right combination of sweetness and tartness. Go for Israeli, if you can, but Spanish will do. "

Kate Barrington-Graham's
CHICKEN WITH GRAND MARNIER AND TARRAGON

(Serves 4)

Ingredients
4 chicken supremes
1 sliced onion
450ml (¾pt) orange juice
300ml (½pt) chicken stock
3 tbsp Grand Marnier
4 sprigs of fresh tarragon or 1 level tbsp dried
Salt and freshly ground pepper
Cooking oil to brown the chicken
Cornflour to thicken
Tarragon sprigs and one orange to garnish

1. Brown the chicken supremes and the sliced onion, then add the liquids and the tarragon, as well as the salt and pepper.
2. Bring to simmering point and cover, cooking gently for 45 minutes to one hour.
3. Thicken with cornflour mixed with orange juice or water and garnish with orange slices or segments and with fresh tarragon.

" I've been makkin this meat roll since I wis a quine in ma mither's kitchen. I hinna changed the recipe ata, so fit ye're gettin here is a genuine turn-o'-the-century meat roll. Ye winna beat it.

Be sure ye get the best steak, and mak sure the bacon's nae ower fatty. Streaky's nae dampt eese ata. Ayr Middle or Back is fit I get. Ye can mince it up yersel. In the aul days, I'd chap up the steak and the bacon wi a richt gweed knife, bit ye can usually persuade yer butcher nooadays, as lang as ye're a weel-kent face, and it's nae near his closin time and he's cleaned oot his mincer.

Ye can pit in the hale packetie o' butter biscuits, bit I sometimes find that maks it a bittie dry. Wi trial and error, I've discovered that if ye tak oot twa and jist hae them wi yer fly cup, and if ye jist pit in the rest, that maks the perfect balance atween moistness and dryness. Ye dinna wint it ower moist, or it winna keep its shape. Ye dinna wint it ower dry, or it winna cut richt and ye'll be left wi a platefae o' crumbs.

I gave awa ma richt meatloaf jars fan I moved in wi Walter and Aggie, so I jist use a Tupperware bowlie, noo, wi a snap-shut lid. Ram the mixture doon ticht. Really ticht. Mak on yer man's come hame late fae the pub.

Be sure and pit a tin plate upside doon on the fit o' yer pan o' watter, or the heat o' yer stove'll melt the Tupperware and what a soss that maks."

Mother Dreep's
MEAT ROLL

Ingredients
400g (1lb) best steak
340g (12oz) lean bacon
1 large onion, chopped finely
1 pkt small butter biscuits, crushed finely
2 eggs, beaten
Sprinkling of nutmeg
A little salt

1. Mince the steak and bacon together. (Your butcher will do this if you ask nicely).
2. Add the onion, biscuit crumbs and beaten eggs, mixing well.
3. Add the seasoning, again mixing well.
4. Fill two 1lb meatloaf jars or a steamer. Place in a pan of boiling water on a trivet or a tin-foil plate and boil for three hours, topping up the water with boiling water as necessary.

" This is my ain recipe for sticky toffee puddin. Ye maybe winna like the coffee essence in it, bit I think it maks it jist special. Wayne and Gibby say this is their favourite puddin and, I must say, I quite like it masel. Cassandra's nae an age til appreciate it yet, bit she clarts it roon her mou and smiles and lachs, so I suppose she likes it, tee.

It is an *affa* sweet puddin, so dinna mak the portions ower big. It's a bittie like chocolate mousse that wye. A little goes a lang road. I heard a mannie on the radio wi Robbie Shepherd sayin that sticky toffee pudding wis Nursery Food, bit fit's wrang wi that?

Ye've ti be sure nae to cook it ower quick. If ye cook it ower quick, the ootside goes as hard as Henderson's and the inside disna cook ata. Keep it slow and ye'll be fine.

Some folk pits in ither kinds o' fruit, nae jist dates. I sometimes pit in bananas, because Gibby likes bananas, bit I've heard o' folk pittin in peaches and strawberries and stuff like that. I widna bother wi that, because they go a' mushy and it tastes like saps.

The sauce is a must. Be sure and powk the puddin a' ower afore ye poor on the sauce. Powk, powk, powk. If the sauce disna get a' through the puddin it comes oot like an affa dry gingerbread. Lik cardboord. Gad sakes. Serve wi cream or custard, bit my favourite is wi a twa-three scoops o' plain ice-cream. A fine mix o' tastes. Het and caul. "

Flo Spurtle's
STICKY TOFFEE PUDDING

(Serves 12)

Ingredients
100g (4oz) soft butter
175g (6oz) soft brown sugar
4 eggs, lightly beaten
225g (8oz) self-raising flour
1 tsp. bicarbonate of soda
2 tbsps. Camp coffee
225g (8oz) stoned dates, finely chopped
300ml (½ pt) boiling water

Syrup
150ml (¼pt) water
50g (2oz) light brown sugar
Large knob of butter
Half a teaspoon vanilla essence
Three tablespoons brandy

Oven
180C 350F Gas 4

1. Line a 23cm (9inch) square or round loose-bottomed tin with a double thickness of grease-proof paper.

2. Cream butter and sugar together and beat in eggs, little by little. Fold in the flour.

3. Mix the bicarbonate of soda and Camp coffee together and pour over the dates in a bowl, followed by the boiling water. Mix and leave to cool a little, before pouring on to the creamed mixture. Use a long-handled wooden spoon to bring together into a runny mixture.

4. Pour into the prepared tin, then place it on a baking sheet and bake for 90 minutes, or until springy to the touch, in a preheated oven.

5. Just before the time is up for the pudding, put all the syrup ingredients in a saucepan. Heat it slowly until the sugar is dissolved. Then bring it to the boil quickly.

6. Take the pudding from the oven and prick it all over with a skewer. Pour the boiling syrup all over and let it stand for five minutes to soak through.

7. Serve with double cream.

" Carrots. Wid ye believe that? Carrots. That's the secret til this cloutie dumplin. They're rare in a potta broth, or gratit in a salad, bit they jist mak this cloutie dumplin something special. A'b'dy says so, bit I dinna tell them the reason. They tak ae bite and they say: 'Oh, Babbie! What fine cloutie dumplin. Fit's yer secret?' Bit I jist keep masel til masel.

Ye taste some affa dry clouties, I aye think. Ye'll be oot in a hotel for yer Christmas denner wi yer femly and they come roon wi this cloutie dumplin, flames leapin aff it like a bleezin lum, and they're obviously affa prood o't, bit it jist tastes lik cardboord. There's nae ony amount o' watery custard'll improve it, eether.

Ye'll see I've said in the recipe ti sprinkle the mixture generously wi flooer afore ye tie it up and bile it. Dinna go daft wi the flooer, though, or it'll turn intil glue and ye'll hae til scrape it affa the dumplin afore ye can store it. It'll mak yer dishtooel affa clarty, as weel.

Ye can eat the dumplin the day ye mak it if ye must, bit I aye think it tastes better stored in a tinnie for a coupla wikks. Let it mature. A dumplin aye tastes better fan it's been sittin. I like mine wi the top o' the milk. I canna be deein wi custard. Bit ye can mak up a sup brandy butter and hae't wi that. If ye're plannin keepin't for a whilie, ye can pit it in the freezer, bit it disna improve the same, storin it in the freezer."

Babbie Girn's
CLOUTIE DUMPLING

(Serves 8)

Ingredients
350g (12oz) plain flour
100g (4oz) fresh white breadcrumbs
225g (8oz) shredded suet
225g (8oz) dark soft brown sugar
1 tsp baking powder
1 tsp mixed spice
1 tsp ground ginger
Half a teaspoon of cinnamon
1 tbsp golden syrup
1 tbsp marmalade
3 tbsp black treacle
1 tbsp milk
Two large carrots (grated)
575g (20oz) dried mixed fruit
Two large eggs, beaten

1. Mix all ingredients together to make quite a firm mixture.
2. Put a large clean tea-towel into a pan of boiling water and boil for one minute. Drain until cool enough to handle, then squeeze dry. Spread on work surface and generously sprinkle with flour. This forms the seal or crust round the dumpling while it is boiling.
3. Spoon the mixture into the middle of the cloth, shaping it into a neat round. Gather up the cloth and tie securely, leaving room for the dumpling to expand slightly.
4. Bring a large pan of water to the boil. Place the dumpling on a trivet or an upturned saucer. Cover and boil for three hours, topping up the water with boiling water as necessary.
5. Remove from pan and leave to stand for five minutes before removing cloth.
6. Serve hot, cut into slices, with cream, custard or brandy butter.

"Puddins is my speciality. The wifie Brose gets really mad fan I win the puddins competition at the WRI wi this recipe, bit the truth often hurts, as they say.

I dinna usually like a bakit cheesecake, bit I like this because it's really easy and quick, and the end result looks like ye've spent oors slavin in yer kitchen. It looks really smashin. Well, ye can see that fae the photie doon below. That wis taen in my kitchen. Really bonnie, isn't it? What a job we hid stoppin Sandy eatin the photiegrapher's aeples.

Onywye, the secret til this recipe is the yoghurt. Mak sure it's natural yoghurt, nae that flavoured stuff. I ken fine the wifie Brose his tried copyin this puddin, bit she hisna managed yet. She disna ken aboot the yoghurt, ye see. Maks a' the difference.

The decoration's really the only fiddly thing aboot it. Mak sure they're crisp American or Canadian aeples. New Zealand Galas is good. Mac Reds is best. Dinna buy French aeples. They're jist bags o' watter. Nae taste aboot them ata. Lik little neeps. Be sure yer knife's sharp, as weel. I get Sandy ti cut the aeple wedges. He's good at that kinna thing. Well, he's aye oot makkin tables and shelves in his sheddie, isn't he?

The glaze is affa easy. If ye wint it a bittie mair tangy, leave oot the honey and try lemon curd, instead. Jist maks it a bittie mair snappy."

Aggie Dreep's
APPLE AND HONEY CHEESECAKE

(Serves 8)

Ingredients
225g (8oz) digestive biscuits, crushed
75g (3oz) unsalted butter
450g (1lb) curd cheese
150ml (5fl oz) plain yoghurt
4 tbsp clear honey
2 eggs
25g (1oz) plain flour
Pinch mixed spice
Grated rind of one lemon
2 red apples, peeled, cored and chopped

For the topping
2 red apples
Lemon juice
150ml (5fl oz) apple juice
2 tsp clear honey
3 tsp arrowroot

Oven
170C   325F   Gas 3.

1. Line the sides of a 21cm (8¹/₂in) loose-bottomed cake tin.
2. Melt the butter, then mix in the crushed digestives. Tip into the cake tin, pressing into the base.
3. Put cheese, yoghurt, honey, eggs, flour, spice and lemon rind into a bowl and beat until smooth. Fold in the chopped apple, then spoon into the tin. Level the surface then bake for about 45 minutes until the cake feels firm. Cool, then remove from the tin.
4. Core and slice thinly the two remaining apples and arrange over the top of the cake. Brush with lemon juice.
5. Put the apple juice and honey into a pan and mix in the arrowroot which has been dissolved in a tablespoon of water. Stir until thick.
6. Leave to cool slightly before pouring over the apple slices, then place in the fridge to set.

      " I dinna ken fit it is aboot ma iced toddy creams, bit Erchie Sotter aye seems ti show up at ma back door fan I'm makkin them, and ye feel kinna obliged ti gie him a tastie. Isn't it an affa coincidence, though? I'm nae sure if it's the cream, or the honey or fit it is.

    I dinna often mak them. Well, I'm only masel and Babbie, ma friend next door, she disna drink an affa lot. Well, I say she disna drink a lot, bit she'll tak a toddy if she's got a dose o' the caul. Babbie smores wi the caul ivry winter. What a toddies she gets through. I often hear singin through the wa, ye ken. Dinna tell onyb'dy else, bit I do. Wailin and singin. And she's nivver in key. If I hear Flower o' Scotland like thon again, I think I'll need ti hae a wordie wi her.

    Onywye, ma iced toddy creams. They're a fine puddin in the summer, bit they heat ye up in the winter, tee. Funny, that, isn't it? And they jist slip doon. Jist like warm velvet. And ye feel like anither een. And anither een. They're affa habit-formin, I wid say.

    I aye use the freshest cream and fine, thicky, sugary honey. Try and get it local instead o' that mass-manufactured stuff. If ye're feelin like a change, ye can use a liqueur instead o' whisky. I sometimes try them wi Cointreau. That's good. Or Tia Maria."

Virginia Huffie's
ICED TODDY CREAMS

(Serves 8-9)

Ingredients
300ml (half a pint) double cream
4 tbsp whisky
3 tbsp thick honey
4 egg yolks

1. Whip cream until quite thick, gradually adding the whisky.

2. Heat honey in a pan or microwave, until hot and runny.

3. Whisk egg yolks in a bowl. Add the hot honey gradually. Continue until mixture is pale. This should now have the same consistency as the cream-and-whisky mixture.

4. Fold both together and divide between eight or nine ramekins, depending on the size.

5. Cover and freeze.

6. Do not remove from the freezer until just before serving, as they don't freeze solid.

" This his taen a lotta persuadin. I dinna reveal my secret recipes til strangers, usually, bit the boy that askit me said it wid appear wi a picture o' me in a best-sellin book o' top North-east cooks, and ye dinna turn awa a chunce lik that ivry day. Me, a celebrity.

So I hope ye appreciate it. This is an award-winnin recipe, this. This is the recipe that's beaten the Wifie Dreep at the Daffodil Tea bakin competition ilky year since 1987. This is a family heirloom recipe, this.

The wifie Dreep's tried copyin this recipe, I ken fine. There's been some affa smells comin oot o' her kitchen. She hisna managed yet because she disna ken the secret. And the secret, atween you and me, is the natural yoghurt.

Dinna bother wi that strawberry-flavoured stuff wi scabby bits o' fruit lyin in the bottom o' the little pottie. You get the best plain yoghurt ye can find. Ye'll be amazed at the taste it gies yer cakie. And what moist. The original recipe didna hae ony vanilla essence in it, bit I quite like it. Ye can leave it oot if that's yer mood.

As for the frostin, well, I suppose ye can buy packet stuff, bit I dinna see the sense in makkin a rare sponge and then clartin it wi that artificial muck. And dinna buy that artificial chocolate, eether. What affa stuff. Get real chocolate. Nithing else. It's a bittie mair fiddly ti work wi, bit the taste's fairly worth it. Num, num, num. "

Geneva Brose's
CHOCOLATE YOGHURT FUDGE CAKE

(Serves 6-8)

Ingredients
Cake
100g (4oz) dark chocolate, not cooking chocolate
175g (6oz) butter
225g (8oz) soft brown sugar
5ml (1tsp) vanilla essence
3 eggs
100g (4oz) natural yoghurt
150g (5oz) self-raising flour

Frosting
75g (3oz) dark chocolate, not cooking chocolate
75g (3oz) butter or low-fat spread
250g (9oz) icing sugar
45ml (3 tbsps) natural yoghurt
Grated chocolate for decoration

Oven
190C 375F Gas 5.

1. Grease and line two 23cm (9-inch) sandwich tins.
2. Break chocolate into a small bowl and melt over a pan of hot water or in microwave.
3. Cream the butter and sugar with the vanilla essence until light and fluffy. Gradually beat in the eggs, then add the yoghurt and chocolate. Gently fold in the flour. Divide mixture between the tins, spreading evenly.
4. Bake for 30-35 minutes, until firm to the touch. Turn out and cool on a wire rack.

Frosting
1. Melt the chocolate with the low-fat spread in a bowl over a pan of hot water or in the microwave. Beat in the icing sugar until smooth. Add the yoghurt and beat until the mixture begins to cool and thicken slightly.
2. Sandwich the cakes together with a little frosting, then spread the remainder over the top and sides. Sprinkle with grated chocolate to decorate.

"I used til like bakin. I wis one o' fit ye micht ca' the stalwarts o' the WRI. I could turn oot a fruit loaf at the drap o' a toorie. Then ma sicht startit goin and I could hardly read ma cookbooks.

'Dinna worry,' said the optician, 'the time will come when your sight won't get any worse. It will stabilise.' Well, I'm still waitin. Not only can I nae read the cookbook noo, I canna hardly *see't* neether. In fact, I canna hardly see the *bowl.* That's led me up some gey calamities, I can tell ye. Vim disna mak affa good icin, tak it fae me. Affa fizzy.

Double shortbreid's aboot the only thing I can really manage nooadays. I can mak this wi ma een closed. I'll maybe *hae* ti mak it wi ma een closed afore lang.

It's really simple and ye'll impress a' yer neighbours because they taste a lot better than thon shop-bocht things.

Some folk mixes up the dough wi widden speens. Some folk sweirs that metal speens is best. Masel, I dinna think ye can beat mixin it up wi yer hauns. Ye get a really good mix that wye. I'm sure that's the secret o' the crumbly biscuit. Melts in yer mou, so they say.

I pits on jist a watter icin; ye dinna wint til obscure the buttery taste o' the shortbreid. Then I pits on a glace cherry, jist so's it'll look bonnie. That can lead til calamities, as weel, though. Still, double shortbreid wi cough sweeties is almost as tasty."

Dorothy Birze's
DOUBLE SHORTBREAD

Ingredients
225g (8oz) plain flour
25g (1oz) cornflour
175g (6oz) butter
75g (3oz) caster sugar

Icing
175g (6oz) icing sugar, sifted
A little warm water to mix.

Oven
170C 325F Gas 3.

1. Put sifted flour, cornflour and caster sugar in a bowl. Rub in butter.
2. Knead until mixture is soft and pliable. Roll out and cut into small rounds with a pastry-cutter.
3. Bake for 30 to 40 minutes.
4. Remove and cool on a wire rack.
5. Mix the icing sugar with the water until smooth, but not runny. Sandwich in pairs with icing and then ice the tops.

" This is nae really bakin. As lang as we get that clear fae the start. Loons dinna bake. Bakin's for quines and cissies. I jist like makkin flapjacks because ye can mak a real mess. Ye can get clartit up til yer elbows and ye dinna get a row because it's something yer mither actually *asks* ye ti dee. I canna mak oot parents ata, sometimes, can you?

My pal, Puddick, and me mak this flapjacks on rainy days in the school holidays.

I canna mind far I learned the recipe. I think it came oot o' a magazine. Ma mither lost her temper wi me ae Sunday and she threw the magazine at me and said: "Awa and dee something useful!" She wis a kinna greety at the time, so I thocht I'd better clear aff.

I picked up the magazine and I saw this recipe, so I thocht I wid gie't a go. We went roon til Puddick's mam's kitchen and she gave us a' the stuff. We hid a rare time. I came back and I presentit ma mither wi a plate o' flapjacks. She looked up. Her een were reed wi greetin. And she jist looked up at me, and she studied the flapjacks and she said: "Fit the hell's that?" Only she said it in a lovin kinda wye. Ye could tell she wis pleased, really.

Ye can really pit onything in them: fruit, oatmeal, treacle. They aye come oot the same and they taste the same. In fact, in the Easter holidays, Puddick hid a bad caul and he sneezed intil the mixture. Naeb'dy tastit ony difference."

Wayne Spurtle's
SQUIDGY RAISIN FLAPJACKS

Ingredients
250g (8oz) porridge oats
125g (4oz) butter
60g (2oz) demerara sugar
1 tbsp. golden syrup
90g (3oz) raisins
1tsp. salt

Oven
180C   350F   Gas 4

1. Grease a shallow, oblong tin 18x28cm (7x11 inches)
2. Melt the butter, sugar and syrup together over a very low heat, stirring them together with a wooden spoon.
3. Remove pan from heat and add oats, raisins and salt and stir well.
4. Pour mixture into the tin and press it down.
5. Bake for 20 minutes.
6. Cut flapjacks into squares and leave to cool before removing them into a tin.

"Personally, I've been a buttery-eater a' ma days. Ye canna beat yer buttery in the mornin, that's fit I aye say. I like them dry; they're a meal in themsels, really. Some folk likes them wi butter. Some likes them wi jam. Some likes them wi jam and butter. Some likes them wi marmalade. Aye, there's a hale wheen o' things ye can dee wi a buttery.

Far did I learn buttery-makkin? Atween the wars, fan I wis an apprentice baker (I'd ti gie't up fan I fun oot I wis allergic til flooer), I measured oot the lard for the butteries and I sweepit the fleer.

Fan the war startit, I'd been promotit fae chief lard-weigher on til mixin up the Yoema Loaf. I miss the fine treacly smells o' the Yoema Loaf. Ye can hardly get it noo. I keep lookin, bit I'm dashed if I can find it.

Onywye, fan the war startit, I volunteered for King and Country. I took the King's Shillin, as ye micht say. It wis a good job I did, for the baker cottoned on til the fact that an affa lot o' his butteries wis disappearin oot the back door. Well, a lad maun mak a poun somewye.

Nooadays, I often rummles up a batch o' butteries til masel. They're healthy, nutritious and they're part o' wir heritage. And kneadin the dough fairly cleans yer hauns."

Erchie Sotter's
BUTTERIES

Ingredients
450g (1lb) sifted strong flour
Half a teaspoon of salt
25g (1oz) yeast or 12g (½oz) dried yeast
A teaspoon of caster sugar
450 ml. (¾ pint) tepid water
225g (8oz) butter
125g (4oz) lard

Oven
200C 400F Gas 6

All ingredients and utensils should be at room temperature before starting to cook.

1. Mix sifted flour and salt in a mixing bowl.
2. Cream the yeast with the sugar in a smaller bowl. When it has frothed up, add the water. (If using dried yeast, activate it according to the maker's instructions.)
3. Add the yeast to the flour, mixing very well. Cover and leave to rise in a warm place for about half an hour until almost doubled in volume.
4. Cream together the butter and lard, then divide into three.
5. Turn the dough out on to a floured surface and roll out into a long strip. Put the first third of the fat mixture in dots on the top third of the dough and fold over like an envelope, as if making puff pastry. Let it rest for 30 minutes, before rolling out.
6. Repeat this procedure twice more until all the fat mixture has been used up and is well absorbed.
7. Roll out and cut into small 15 ovals / rounds and put on to a floured baking sheet, leaving 5cm. (2 inches) between each one to allow for spreading.
8. Cover and leave to rise for almost an hour, before baking for 20-25 minutes.

"It wis my great-grandmither that learned me makkin oatcakes. I often think back til the days afore the war and my great-grandmither; her lang, black frockie sweepin ower the steen slabs in the kitchen wi the fairm lads sittin roon the great widden table in the corner, haein their fly cup.

And she'd be there, stannin ower the fire, amon a' thon heat, turnin oot oatcake, efter oatcake, efter oatcake. And ivry one wis perfect. Nae automation in them days. Bakers nooadays? They're hardly bakers ata. Computers dis the lot. A traveller telt me that. They jist push a button and – whoosh – oot comes a tray o' funcies. Ye canna hardly believe it, can ye?

Bit that wis my great-grandmither for ye. A richt strong woman. Fifteen kids in twelve year and hardly broke intil a sweat. Ma great-grandfather did a' the sweatin, I suppose. I dinna mind muckle aboot him. I can jist vaguely mind a little bent aul mannie sittin twa-faul in the corner, gigglin til himsel and lachin. I suppose haein fifteen kids must tak it oot o' ye.

Onywye, it wis ma great-grandmither that learned me oatcakes. Dinna hae the heat up ower high, that's the secret. I like makkin mine wi butter, bit ye're really supposed ti use lard for a genuine North-east oatcake. I eat mine on a Sunday at teatime. I like it wi a slab o' mature cheddar. Cheese and *breid*, it's ca'ed. I'm nae richt sure o' the reason."

Ebenezer Grip's
OATCAKES

Ingredients
450g (1lb) medium oatmeal
1 level tsp salt
1 level tsp bicarbonate of soda
90g (3oz) butter and margarine mixed
Around 150mls (5 fl oz) hot, but not boiling, water

Oven
200C   400F   Gas 6

1. Sieve the bicarbonate into the oatmeal and salt. Add the fat mixture, cut into three or four pieces. Pour on the hot water. Mix with a knife until the fat melts.
2. Tip out the mixture and knead lightly, until it matches the consistency of pastry. Roll out to a square or rectangle shape.
3. When the mixture has cooled, cut into about 24 pieces and lift on a fish slice on to baking trays.
4. Bake for about 40 minutes in the pre-heated oven, turning them half-way through. Lift off carefully and cool on a wire rack.

Stronach:
the
glossary

Aa: *All* (Pop music's aa the rage nooadays).

Ae: *One* (Jist ae biled agg this mornin, please, my sweet).

Affa: *Awfully, awful* (What an affa day o' rain).

Afore: *Before* (Afore ye sit doon at the tea table, ye'd better wash yer hands).

Ain: *Own* (Babbie's ower ill-natered for her ain good).

Ata, ava: *At all* (The minister's nae lookin weel ata).

Aul: *Old* (Mrs Barrington-Graham winna say how aul she is).

Aweel: *Well* (Aweel, I'd better leave before the bill comes).

Aye: *Always* (I aye thocht there wis something funny aboot Erchie Sotter).

Backit: *Reversed* (Sandy's car has backit intil a tree).

Bairn: *Child* (Wayne acts the hard man, but he's really a bairn).

Ben: *Through* (Geneva's baking ben in the kitchen).

Big Bugs: *VIPs* (Cooncillors fairly think they're big bugs).

Birl: *Spin* (Babbie birls at the eightsome reel lik a wifie demented).

Bittie: *Bit* (Gibby's nae a bad lad; he's jist a bittie confused).

Black affrontit: *Embarrassed:* (Dorothy ate like a pig. I wis black affrontit).

Bocht: *Bought* (Sammy bocht Floretta a lovely engagement ring).

Bools in her mou: *Plummy accent:* (Mrs Barrington-Graham has bools in her mou).

Boord: *Board* (Erchie was so drunk he was as stiff as a boord).

Bowf: *Bang, bark* (Flo hit Gibby – BOWF – across the face).

Briks: *Trousers* (What a rare pair of tartan briks Aggie is sporting today)

Brocht: *Brought:* (Fit hiv you brocht til the kirk sale o' work?).

Ca: *Call* (Fit d'ye ca Babbie's nephew fae Tarland?).

Ca: *Shove* (Ca that broken-doon car up til the garage).

Cairt: *Cart* (Sandy's cairt has two flat tyres).

Canna be deein wi: *Can't abide.* (I canna be deein wi skirlie and custard).

Canna see't masel: *Can't see it myself* (They say Gibby's handsome. I canna see't masel).

Cantrips: *Capers* (Wayne gets up to all sorts of cantrips).

Cauler: *Colder* (Ebenezer Grip's hert is cauler nor ice).

Chestie: *Chest* (Cassandra's little chestie sounds really wheezy).

Chikky: *Cheeky* (Wayne Spurtle's a chikky monkey).

Clooks: *Claws* (Floretta's got her clooks in a new boyfriend).

Clort: *Reprehensible individual* (That insurance man's jist a clort).

Conniched: *Absolutely worn out.* (Erchie would still be a womaniser, but he's conniched)

Crackit: *Cracked* (My chamberpot is crackit).

Craw: *Crow* (Aggie Dreep's an aul craw).

Dampt: *Polite form of "damned"* (Dampt if I ken).

Darker, tak a: *Go mad:* (If I get drunk again, Geneva will tak a darker).

Dee: *Do, Die* (I dinna ken fit Walter wid dee if I dee next week).

Dinna: *Don't* (The bus winna wait, so dinna be late).

Div: *Do?* (Div ye like lemon cheesecake, or d'ye prefer skirlie?).

Divvlement: *Devilment* (There's a lotta divvlement in Wayne Spurtle)

Doon aboot the mou: *Depressed* (Flo's lookin affa doon aboot the mou)

Draan: *Drawn* (Come and look at the bonnie picter Cassandra's draan).

Drappie: *Small amount of liquid* (I'll tak a drappie whisky – jist ti keep ye company)

Dreel: *Drill or Row* (We're hoping for a twa-three dreel o' new tatties).

Dubs: *Mud* (Wayne has been playing in the dubs again).

Ee: *You* (And fa the hell are ee?).

Eeseless: *Useless* (Walter is as eeseless as a chocolate fireguard).

Expeckin: *Pregnant* (I see the wifie Broon's expeckin again).

Fa?: *Who?* (Fa said *you* could bake?).

Fae: *From* (Far d'ye come fae?)

Fairm: *Farm* (Wester Boggiedubs is the biggest fairm in the Howe of Stronach).

Fan?: *When?* (I'll pay the bill fan I get paid).

Far?: *Where?* (Far d'ye think you're gaun?).

Feart: *Frightened:* (Walter would stand up to Aggie, but he's feart).

Fecht: *Fight* (I'll fecht ye for the last cream bun).

Feel: *Idiot, stupid* (Gibby Spurtle's a complete feel).

Femly: *Family* (The Spurtles are a queer femly).

Fermer-chiel: *Rural rustic male person* (Erchie Sotter's a fermer-chiel).

Fit?: *What?* (Fit *is* the capital o' Outer Mongolia?).

Fit wye?: *Why?* (Fit wye his Erchie Sotter got lipstick on his collar?).

Fitivver: *Whatever:* (Fitivver Gibby Spurtle says is usually rubbish).

Fly cup: *Elevenses:* (Come in past for a fly cup. The kettle's on).

Foo?: *How?* (Foo wid ye like a clap in the lugs?).

Fool: *Dirty* (Wayne Spurtle usually has a fool face).

Forbye: *Besides* (You could smell him through the hoose, and for miles roon forbye).

Fower: *Four* (Mrs Barrington-Graham his fower TVs in her hoose).

Fowk: *Folk* (There's nithing as queer as fowk).

Funcy, funcy piece: *Small fresh cake* (Tak anither funcy; they're affa fine).

Gadgie: *Chap* (That gadgie's startin til annoy me).

Gaun: *Going* (It's twa in the mornin. You should be gaun hame).

Gawpit: *Of low intelligence* (Gibby Spurtle's as gawpit as a stunned sheep).

Get on wi't: *Don't delay* (The dishes winna wash themsels, so get on wi't).

Gey: *Estimable:* (Sandy Brose has a gey job on his hands wi Geneva for a wife).

Gie's: *Hand over* (Gie's twa bugs o' yer honey lumps)

Girn: *Moan, whine, grumble* (Ma mither likes nothing better than a good girn).

Gled: *Glad* (I'm richt gled ti see ye).

Golden staircase, up the: *Dead* (Ma mither went up the golden staircase in 1947).

Greetin: *Crying* (Wayne disna like onybody seein him greetin)

Gweed: *Good* (This fish isna gweed. Are ye sure it's fresh?).

Hake: *Search* (I'm awa for a hake in the January sales).

Hale: *Whole* (Would you like a hale softie and syrup, or perchance jist a half?).

Happie-up: *Covering of clothes* (That's a skimpy bikini. Ye need mair o' a happie-up).

Heatie-up: *Second cup of tea* (Are ye for a heatie-up?).

Heid: *Head* (Miss Pink hisna a heid for heights).

Heid bummers: (See "big bugs").

Hert: *Heart* (Virginia Huffie's got a richt saft hert).

Het: *Hot* (I'll leave ma tea five minutes. It's affa het).

Howe: Hollow (I stay in the Howe of Stronach).

Humphin: *Labouring* (I'm humphin bugs o' tatties up at the fairm this wikk).

Hunder: *Hundred* (Supposin ye wait a hunder year, I winna mairry ye).

Ilky: *Every* See "Ivry".

Ivnoo: *Just now* (I'd offer ye a sup tea, but I've nae teabags in the hoose ivnoo).

Ivry: *Every* (Gibby Spurtle's oot drinkin ivry nicht).

Joollery: *Jewellery* (Kate Barrington-Graham's usually drippin wi joollery).

Ken: *Know* (I ken yer mither's ugly, bit you dinna tak efter her).

Kinna: *Kind of* (He's a kinna stupid-lookin, really).

Kitchie-deem: *Kitchen help, young and female* (Virginia was once a kitchie-deem).

Knivs: *Fists* (Gibby Spurtle's knivs are like hammers).

Lach: *Laugh* (Ye'll nivver get a lach oot o' Ebenezer Grip).

Lassie: *Girl* See "Quine".

Lavvie: *Water-closet* (Mam! I'm needin the lavvie!).

Lik: *Like* (Dinna you look at me lik I've three heids).

Lookit: *Looked* (I lookit and lookit, bit I couldna see yer tattie-pot).

Mair: *More* (Ony mair nonsense fae you and ye're oot)

Makkin: *Making* (Gibby's makkin a pest o' himsel again).

Maun: *Must* (Ye maun come in and see me in the hospital).

Meenit: *Minute* (Ye can surely wait anither meenit).

Min: *Chap* (Hey, min, shift yer car!).

Mony: *Many* (There's ower mony folk in the toon nooadays).

Mou: *Mouth* (Aggie Dreep has a mou on her like the Don).

Muckle: *Much* (I'd go on ma holidays, bit I hinna muckle cash).

Nicht: *Night* (Flo Spurtle works day and nicht because Gibby's unemployed).

Nivver: *Never* (I've nivver seen bigger drawers on a washin-line than Aggie's).

Nooadays: *Nowadays* (Fit's young Sammy deein nooadays?).

Nor: *Than* (I ken mair aboot bakin nor you).

Nowt: *Cattle* (That's some richt fine nowt up at Wester Boggiedubs).

Ony: *Any* (Hiv you ony spare sugar? I ve run oot.)

Or: *Until* (I'm standing here or Gibby comes to pick me up).

Ory: *Vulgar, filthy* (What an ory mannie Erchie Sotter is in his personal habits).

Ower the heid: *Excessive* (She's got kids ower the heid).

Peety: *Pity* (What a peety Babbie's budgie flew intil the hoover)

Peyed: *Paid* (Hiv ye heard fit Mrs Barrington-Graham peyed for her new frock?).

Picter: *Picture* (That Mona Lisa's a richt bonnie picter).

Plout: *Hit* (Dee that again and I'll plout ye).

Poun: *Pounds* (That car cost three hunder and fifty poun).

Pubbie: *Public house:* (I'm affa thirsty. I'm awa til the pubbie).

Puckle: *Small collection:* (I dug up a puckle carrots fae the gairden).

Quaet: *Quiet* (I wid jist like five minutes' peace and quaet).

Quine: *Girl* (Babbie's 68, though she thinks she's still a young quine).

Rare: *Marvellous:* (What a rare frock Mrs Barrington-Graham wore til the kirk social).

Reemin ower: *Full to excess:* (The lavvie's blockit and the pan's reemin ower).

Rikkin: *Steaming, smoking* (The dung up at the fairm is so fresh it's still rikkin).

Roch: *Rough* (Gibby was out for a stag party last night and he looks really roch)

Roon: *Round* (Erchie wis that drunk he birled roon and roon and fell in a heap)

Sasser: *Saucer* (Erchie Sotter drinks his tea oot o' the sasser).

Scaffie: *Refuse collector* (The scaffie comes ilky Monday and Thursday).

Seener: *Sooner* (The seener ye leave, the seener ye'll be back).

Selt: *Sold* (Ebenezer Grip selt twa ton o' tatties last month).

Shottie: *Shot* (Could I hae a shottie o' yer frilly nightie?).

Sic: *Such* (It's sic a caul day, I'd better pit on ma woolly drawers).

Siller: *Money* (Ebenezer Grip makes plenty siller in his shop).

Smeddum: *Spirit, strength of character* (Babbie Girn has plenty smeddum).

Smit: *Infect:* (Dinna come ower close; I'll smit ye wi the flu).

Smorin: *Choking:* (I'm jist smorin wi the caul).

Soor: *Sour* (Hiv ye ony soor sweeties left?).

Sotter: *Mess* (What a sotter Dorothy's gairden's in).

Spew: *Sick:* (That wifie Barrington-Graham maks me spew).

Spile: *Spoil* (Ye spile tattie soup if ye pit in garlic).

Spleet-new: *Brand new* (Far did Walter get the cash for a spleet-new car?)

Splutten: *Split* (That tree wis splutten in twa wi lichtnin).

Spurtle: *Stick for stirring porridge* (She has legs like a spurtle).

Stap: *To stuff* (Mrs Barrington-Graham staps her face like she's eatin her last meal).

Stramash: *Violent encounter* (What a stramash at the pub on Friday nicht).

Sup, Suppie: *Small amount:* (Will ye tak a sup whisky in yer tea?).

Swick: *Cheat* (Dinna play cards wi Ebenezer; he's a swick).

Taen: *Taken* (Somebody's taen aff wi ma man and I canna say I'm sorry).

Tak: *Take* (Tak yer hands aff my knees ony time ye like).

Tastit: *Tasted* (That milk tastit soor).

Teem: *Empty* (I wid offer ye mair tea, bit the pottie's teem)

Tekkie: *Flying visit* (I took a tekkie in past the art gallery this mornin).

Telt: *Told* (I telt him he wis wastin his time askin me hame).

The morn: *Tomorrow* (I'll pey ye the morn, I promise).

The Toon: *Aberdeen* (Gibby's in The Toon lookin for a new job).

Thegither: *Together* (Sammy and Floretta are gaun thegither).

Thocht: *Thought* (I *thocht* I'd seen him afore).

Thochtfae: *Thoughtful* (Gibby's really thochtfae. He warms my side o' the bed).

Thole: *Endure* (The best poultice is as het as ye can thole).

Thon: *That* (Thon's nivver fresh-baked scones. Thon's oot o' a freezer).

Ticht: *Tight* (Babbie's new stays are a bittie ticht for her).

Timmer in aboot: *Chastise* (I got really bad service, so I jist timmered them in aboot).

Tooterin: *Idling* (Gibby disna work. He spends his time tooterin aboot).

Topper: *Wonderful chap* (My doctor's jist a topper).

Tummled: *Tumbled* (Babbie wis so tired she jist tummled intil her bed)

Tyauve: *To labour hard* (It's a sair tyauve for a half-loaf)

Wheesht: *Be quiet!* (Stop that noise! Wheesht!).

Wikk: *Week* (Teachers get 12 wikks holidays ilky year. It's nae nearly enough).

Wrang: *Wrong* (Fit's wrang wi Ebenezer the day? He's smilin).

Yatterin: *Incessant chatter* (Aggie wid win the Olympic Gold for yatterin).

We hope you have enjoyed your short stay with the people of Stronach. You can keep up with all their adventures and activities every Saturday morning in the Press and Journal.

Next autumn, Volume 2 of the Stronach stories will be published. And the first Stronach tape will be released, with tales from books One and Two, in the perfect format for friends abroad.

For further details, or if you just want to tell us what you thought of your book and what you would like to see in future, we'd be delighted to hear from you.

Send an SAE to:

Alison Reid, Stronach Media Ltd., Tullynessle, AB33 8QN.